TRAVELS
Near and Far Out

TRAVELS

Near and Far Out

BY ANTHONY CARSON

With a Preface by EVELYN WAUGH

Pantheon Books *New York*

A DIVISION OF RANDOM HOUSE

⎍⎍⎍⎍⎍⎍⎍⎍⎍⎍

PREFACE

THERE are two conditions in which a preface by another hand may be desirable for the work of a living author; neither of them applies to Mr. Carson.

It may be that the book is obscure and the reader needs hints to its understanding. Mr. Carson writes with exquisite lucidity.

Or it may be that the author makes personal claims for which a guarantee of good faith is required from a third party. This I cannot give. I have never had the honour of meeting Mr. Carson, I know nothing about him except what he himself reveals and I can only conjecture what degree of credulity he postulates in his readers. Are these sketches, autobiographical in form, pure fantasy? Is there really a man so fortunate as to have enjoyed these extravagant experiences in anything corresponding to the version presented? The mystery is impenetrable. Can Mr. Carson really be, as he claims, a German? His humour, so light and poetic, seems essentially English, but perhaps there is something Teutonic about his yearning for the Mediterranean. One claim, I think, can be established from internal evidence. Although it is only in the last decade that he has made himself widely known, he cannot be a young man. He belongs to the *ancien régime*. There is no whine of the underdog in his work. His associates are almost all of the underworld; his own condition is precarious; his morality, as he describes it, is extremely loose; but he betrays no resentment or scorn of those whose habits are more orderly. He is a hedonist and a sensualist joyfully celebrating the huge variety of life. There is something of Norman Douglas in him, something of Firbank, nothing at all of the "sick" or the "beat."

All I can say to the American reader is something already well known to the English: that here is an artist to be *enjoyed*, to be read uncritically without any concern for dark trends or symbols; a man who does what he sets out to do with complete mastery. His work is all fragmentary and therefore apt for selection. This volume offers a fair sample of it. Those who are ensnared will find the charm anything but transient. They will ask for more and find it gratefully.

EVELYN WAUGH

CONTENTS

vii

CONTENTS

viii

Contents

PART ONE

ⅬⅡⅡⅢⅡⅡⅢⅡⅡⅢ

A ROSE
BY ANY OTHER NAME

I WAS BORN in Hampstead and lived in Canfield Gardens. I can remember my father only vaguely. As he used to climb the stairs he dropped pennies all over the place and seemed upset when I scrambled to pick them up. One of his favourite jokes was about a small man at a party who said "Certainly, I am fond of animals, I keep a bee." He produced plays with music, and I remember one which was apparently about China and Japan. There were naval officers and a song scene with temple bells. I went to see it five times, and for a certain number of years I thought most of the actors came from Hong Kong—even though I was allowed to go back-stage and see them take off their make-up. My brother, who was six years older than myself (and who had already actually played a tiny part in this play, saying "Give me an orange"), did not correct this belief, but kept the mystification growing by suggesting the audience were mostly Chinese, as well. Then, suddenly, my father broke with the East and began to produce plays with men who never took off their hats on the stage and who were always forgiving their sons and daughters. "America," explained my brother. The house in Canfield Gardens was full

3

of cigar smoke and men called Abe who gave me double-barrelled water pistols and called me "Sonny."

On the arrival of the First World War, men in bowler hats and raincoats visited the house and started searching the rooms.

"What are you doing?" cried my mother.

"We are looking for certain documents," said one of the men, removing his bowler hat. "We represent Scotland Yard."

"What documents?" asked my mother.

"Letters from the Kaiser," said the inspector.

"The Kaiser," repeated my mother in amazement. "Why on earth should we have letters from the Kaiser?"

"Because we have ascertained that your husband is the Kaiser's cousin," replied the inspector.

My mother protested about this and kept weeping.

"My husband has just volunteered for service with the British Expeditionary Force," she said.

"That is what first aroused our suspicions," said the policeman.

They searched the house quite thoroughly and walked off with a copy of Nietzsche and a volume of Schopenhauer. We never saw them again.

This visit by the police could be explained by the fact that the family name was von Falkenhausen, with which name I had been born. We possessed a coat of arms and cutlery engraved with coronets, and there was vague talk of enormous castles and of a sinister member of the von Falkenhausen family who was some sort of priest. But my father hardly ever talked about his family, and it was only much later that I heard, in a very roundabout way, that the von Falkenhausens were descended from the Ludwigs of Bavaria.

When I reached the age of seven I was packed off to a preparatory school in Sussex while my parents made a trip to America, where the sort of plays my father produced were then in great vogue. The preparatory school was quite a stately building with the usual playing fields, and gave on to the Downs and fields of mustard flecked with poppies. You could smell the sea and there was an incessant trilling of larks and the rasp of rooks.

"Ah," said the headmaster, a very tall man with a military moustache, "Anthony von Falkenhausen. Welcome, my little man," and he patted me on the head and led me into his study, where he lit a pipe and gave me a short talk on the rules of junior life. "Play fair with life, little man, and it will play fair with you." Then I was given to the matron and shown a bed in the dormitory and went down to the dining-room for cocoa.

Quite near the school was a barracks for Indian soldiers. I soon learned that numbers were dying rapidly, carried off by some mysterious disease—possibly connected with fresh air from the Downs—and it became quite commonplace to hear the slow coils of the Funeral March unwind from a trumpet, with the hopeless throb of a drum. I hadn't been long at the school before some of the boys started shouting "German spy! German spy!" The cry was taken up and it was actually suggested, even believed, that I was helping to blow up shipping in the English Channel and that I signalled from the dormitory with a torch to Hun submarines. One of the masters actually asked me to help him translate sentences from a German grammar, although I didn't know a word of the language, and he sometimes greeted me conspiratorially with *"Guten Tag"* when we passed each other alone in the corridors. "The Germans are good chaps at heart," he told me once.

The headmaster, Mr. Carter, disappeared from time to time to fight at the Front and always returned to the school looking very cheerful, his arm in a sling, or hobbling on a stick and with a touch or two of shrapnel which he threw off in no time at all. Each time he appeared, hobbling to his study, he bent down and patted me on the head and said "And how are we, little man?" The fourth time he returned from France he didn't look quite so well; his face was grey, and he was coughing quite a bit; but he still bent down and patted me on the head. It was some time later that we heard that he had been gassed, and it took him at least a month to recover enough to take his cold baths and lead paper-chases on the Downs.

One day I received a letter from my mother telling me that my father had decided to stay in New York, where he was having a good success with his plays, that he had again volunteered for the army, and had again been searched for letters from the Kaiser, but this time by men in their shirt-sleeves smoking cigars. He had taken out naturalisation papers, which meant that I now had an American father. I told this to some of the boys, but it didn't make very much difference: non-English countries were all much the same—it could just as well have been America which had been gassing our headmaster and filling him with shrapnel. My mother also told me that she intended coming over to England as soon as she could, but that she had been terribly put off by some of my postcards, which depicted a terrible shipwreck and which I had sent during our duty letter-writing days.

One day Mr. Carter sent for me to his study and I sat down in the chair on the other side of his desk. He seemed rather embarrassed and was puffing furiously at an old black pipe which he generally only used for the Front.

"How's the little man?" he asked.

"Very well, sir," I answered.

"I have some news for you," he said, "something that may perhaps change the course of your life."

"Yes, sir?" I said.

"After all, what's in a name, as Shakespeare said. You remember that bit?"

6

"Yes, sir," I said.

"Can you name the play?" asked Mr. Carter, puffing clouds of smoke.

"*Romeo and Juliet*," I said.

"Well done, little man," said the headmaster. "And now to the subject in hand. We've decided to change *our* name."

"Our name, sir?" I said. "Do you mean the school?"

"No," said Mr. Carter, "your name. It is no longer von Falkenhausen. Not that that isn't a good name, of course, and I'm the last person to dislike the Boches. Between ourselves, I really prefer them to the French. But things in the world are a bit strained at the moment. So your name is now going to be Anthony Carson."

"Yes, sir," I said.

"You'll soon get used to it," said the headmaster, digging into his pipe. When I got up to leave, he accompanied me to the door.

"Goodbye, Anthony Carson," he said, patting my head.

The next day we went for a walk on the Downs, winding up and down the old green shoulders of chalk, the sky pricked with larks. After two hours' walking, we rested by a dew-pond and looked down into the valley, toy-like with miniature trees. While we sat there, an old gentleman approached us, his eyes shining with the rheum of nostalgia, the ache for the days of bare-legged boys and sardines in the dormitory. He stood still, scanning us like a lost tribe, and then his eye fell on me. Moving towards me, he patted me on the head and bent down.

"And what's your name, little man?" he asked. I thought for a moment, but not for long.

"Anthony Carson," I said.

"A fine old English name," said the elderly gentleman. "A very fine old English name."

But as he moved away, I felt suddenly trapped in the com-

7

plexity of names and identities and shouted out: "My real name is von Falkenhausen!"

That evening after prep I had to write about five hundred times: "My name is Anthony Carson. My name is Anthony Carson. My name is . . ."

⎍⎍⎍⎍⎍⎍⎍⎍⎍

A YEAR IN THE STATES

AFTER I had left my public school, my mother decided that she, my brother and myself would go to America, where my father was producing a sort of musical play about China or Japan called *Eastward Ho!* My brother was all ready to conquer New York and spent a lot of the time on the journey writing the first act of a very sinister play. He was so pleased with it that he insisted on reading it to my mother, who, already sea-sick, confined herself to her cabin for the rest of the voyage.

My brother, Conrad, did not want more than one dramatist in the family and always steered me clear of anything to do with the footlights. It was natural history for me. Already, thanks to Conrad, I knew far more about prehistoric animals than was good for a growing boy, had studied the insides of ants and peered through a microscope at unicellular plant life.

"America," said Conrad, as we stood on the boat-deck gazing at the tilting horizon, "is full of animals."

"I know," I said.

"Bears, turtles, rattlesnakes and racoons," he continued; "the country is one vast zoo."

"What about the people?" I asked not very hopefully.

9

"Leave the people to me," said Conrad.

Eventually we saw Belle Island come out of the sea and soon we were sailing up the St. Lawrence River. From Quebec we took a train to New York. Almost immediately my brother, first act and all, was swallowed up in it, and I saw him only in snatches, ringing up actresses and millionaires and looking more and more like Broadway. I have always envied him those six years of seniority; they are still a gap in my life; I have never found them. "You must go to school," my mother told me, "it's no good your hanging around New York at your age." I was sent to a school in Massachusetts called Pinkerton Academy, equipped with native clothes and seen off by my family. "Study the fauna," shouted my brother, waving his opera-hat, and the train left for the semi-English unknown.

Pinkerton Academy turned out to be a large white building at the foot of a sort of smallish mountain. It immediately reminded me of a hotel, had lifts, a ballroom, cinema and tiled swimming pool where you could buy sundaes and sodas. I was greeted at the door by an enormously distinguished man of about sixty wearing pince-nez attached to a black cord. He could have been a famous Chopin executant, a fashionable philosopher, but made me think most of the figure who then pointed out from American magazines, saying LET ME BE YOUR FATHER. "Welcome to Pinkerton," said this philosopher-father, holding out his hand and then putting his arm round my shoulders and guiding me down the hall to his study. "We greet you as a symbol of the unbreakable bond between our two great English-speaking peoples."

"Thank you," I said.

"You are a representative," he continued, "of nearly the greatest country on earth, and one that we all, masters and boys alike, are apt to consider as our mother-land."

I was taken up in one of the lifts by a small man whose massive horn-rimmed glasses made his eyes owlish. "I will take you to your room," he said, and I followed him along a creamy passage to a door marked 22. He unlocked it and gave a slight bow. "There is a bathroom, and the headmaster's wife has sent up these roses." He pointed to a bowl of flowers on a table.

"How frightfully nice of her," I said.

"I hope you will extract constructive benefit from your stay in our academy," he added. "I am the General Knowledge professor."

After I had unpacked there was a knock on the door and a tallish boy in knickerbockers entered the room.

"Howdy," he said. "My name's Jackson. You the limey?"

"Yes," I said.

"You a fairy?"

"No," I said.

"Well, why the goddamned blooms?"

"The headmaster's wife had them sent up," I said.

"Well I'll be . . ." said Jackson. "You're a fast worker for a limey. Got a flask?"

"No," I said. "Why?"

"Why?" cried Jackson with a shout. "Just a moment."

A minute later he returned with four other boys and he told them about the flask and the headmaster's wife. Two of them took out flasks from their hip-pockets and we began drinking and then another boy produced a flask and we drank again and then we started singing. Finally there was a tapping at the door, and the professor of General Knowledge peered into the room.

"You guys are making a bit of noise," he said. "I'm trying to correct the psychology papers."

"Come in and have a drink, Prof," said Jackson, holding out his flask.

"O.K., just one," said the professor, but it was hours before I went to bed.

The curriculum of the academy was more or less the same as in other adolescent schools of America—French, English, History, Mathematics, Anglo-American Literature and a sort of armour-plated football which, by its novelty and its use of involved code numbers, was tribal, brutal and intriguing. While in an English public school I had been considered stupid, dense and anonymous, here I suddenly found myself at the top of the class in every subject, was presented with an inscribed hip-flask, had a choice of three girls for the Commem balls, and in no time at all was being invited to rattlesnake parties, the most select social functions of the Academy.

At the back door of the Academy, sloping up to the top of the mountain, was a wild rockery of scarlet azaleas and a perpetual ballet of butterflies, which seemed to have flown off the bushes like petals in a summer dream. Among the bushes, in nooks and crevices in the stones, lived the rattlesnakes, and as one walked, equipped with glove and forked stick, the air buzzed with signals of death. After a cautious prodding with the stick, a snake coiled out, was pinned by the neck, killed and skinned. On most of these expeditions I was accompanied by Jackson, who, in the two years he had been at the Academy, had caught nearly two thousand rattlers.

Later on I met a boy called Travers, who was editor of the school magazine. He was tall, thin and elegant and wore long fair hair.

"I never thought an Englishman would go crazy about rattlesnakes," he said. "Nelson didn't hunt for snakes, nor William Pitt, nor Shelley, nor William Wordsworth."

"I am going to be a naturalist," I said.

"Animals are the most boring things on earth," said Travers. "They're even more boring than girls, though I admit girls talk. Why don't you try thinking a little and write something for the magazine?"

In no time at all I abandoned the rattlesnakes, though with

some feeling of guilt (and to this day I move backwards and forwards between snakes and symbols of thought), and started to compose small and terrible poems for the magazine. Finally I started to write a play, and actually finished the first act.

When I returned to New York for the winter vacation I found the flat crammed with birds. There were whip-poor-wills, Mexican thrushes, Javanese robins, finches, and a sort of hawk. There were also tanks full of terrapins. My brother sat there day after day staring at them and he was even studying Audubon's treatise on ornithology. "New York's a hard city," he said. I went on writing my play but my brother wouldn't listen to it, so I read it to my mother. A year later we returned to England with lizards, tortoises, racoons and all the birds, and the wash-basins in our cabins were filled with turtles. Half-way across the Atlantic my brother started writing another play. "Study this," he said to me, handing over Audubon's treatise on ornithology.

Years later, in the South of France, I met Jackson and Travers again. They were exactly alike, both pairs of eyes photoelectric behind rimless glasses, under prosperous hats, their words identically spherical, unattached and factory assembled.

MY FIRST AFFAIR

MY MOTHER and brother, since my father was in New York, had sent me to a crammer's to prepare to enter Oxford and there was football, a beautiful countryside and a rather keen inter-house competition in schoolboy erotics. I then retired, with my family, to Partridge Green in Sussex, a young failure. My brother had come from Oxford with brilliant debts and prevailed on my mother to send me to New Zealand. "Like a convict," said my brother, lighting an Abdulla, "but he will no doubt end up owning millions of sheep."

I sailed to New Zealand on a government-sponsored passage with a group of about thirty other lost youths and arrived in Auckland, where we were met by a clergyman who gave us a talk about opportunity and clean living. Then we were seen off to our respective employers. Mine was in South Island, and it meant another sea journey between the two islands and a rail trip to the township of Wakatipu. This lay beside a great jewel-blue lake with a snow-capped mountain behind it, and I felt a flicker of joy, the old joy of spoon-fishing and forests, and owls at night and a secret nymph behind the spicy bracken. The nearest thing I had ever got to one of these was fumbling with a plump girl called Brenda at Partridge Green. (When, much later, I really met the true nymph of the forest I never got over it.)

My sheep station was at the head of the lake, and when I arrived there I found that I was one of about ten brand-new English roustabouts who had all failed their exams. They were given jobs as assistant cowmen, vegetable-garden weeders, assistant ditch-tenders and, least popular of all, dag-men, which implied following around any one of 20,000 sheep and snipping off dung. I was relegated to cows and the care of a huge Friesian bull who used to stare, brooding, at the ground like an angry old poet, and who had lately killed a Swedish cook.

"The cook was drunk," explained the head cowman, "and offered the animal some whisky."

"I'll never do that," I promised.

Among the failed English scholars was a tall spectacled man called Julius Bronson. He had studied in some sort of seminary and had, it was rumoured, been expelled for startling behaviour. "I can't bear animals," he told us, "mainly because of the smell." He dressed better than any of us, and hung his room with prints and crucifixes, and even pieces of brocade. While the rest of us drank beer in Hawea or went to dances in Wakatipu looking for nymphs and fighting with the locals, Bronson sat in his room reading Milton. On Sundays, and certain saints' days, he burned incense. He was a hard worker and had been drafted to vegetables, which he disliked only a little less than animals (except for vegetable marrows). Later he specialised in flowers. This was possible because the owner of the sheep station was a millionaire, and it helped his prestige when his wife gave masses of home-grown flowers to charity, even though the station was running at a loss. All this was perfectly reasonable, the Milton and the flowers, the incense, the vegetable marrows and the brocade. Everywhere else it was the Twenties, and Bronson would have been in his element, tan-

gled up with High-Church liturgies and cynical saxophones.
But to us, lost public-school boys among mountains where
parrots ate sheep, he was a sort of goad; and he often came
back to his room to find it crammed with sheep, or rhubarb,
or hay.

After a time we all began to drift away, and a year later
I found myself in Christchurch, selling disinfectant. I lived
in a sort of suburb, in a neat white bungalow with a small rose
garden in a street called Regent Street. The house was called
Kia Ora, and belonged to an old lady by the name of Mrs.
Softcup. She had a daughter called Kate who was about thirty
and who sang. The family had arrived from London about
three years earlier and found little difference between Christchurch and Wimbledon, except perhaps that Christchurch was
more English. Kate had been married to some sort of Shake-
spearean actor and Mrs. Softcup told me that he was atro-
ciously wicked. At first Kate had just been a woman in a house,
but gradually I began to see her face only in a sort of haze, and
within the haze was the nymph behind the mountains and the
mysterious plump girl of Partridge Green. Kate worked in a
gramophone shop, and I began to long for the evenings when
she came back to Kia Ora from work and filled the house with
lovely doubts and problems and could be secretly fitted with
myths. I sold no disinfectant, and wrote poems.

Kate took no notice of me at all. She had a friend who came
to the house called Mr. Lennox. He was a small man with a
toothbrush moustache and a bowler hat and he always carried
an attaché case full of papers with estimates. He could prune
roses, make chicken runs, mend plugs and fuses and talk
fluently about the reasonable things of this world. I envied
him. He disliked me at first sight and used to trip me up in
conversation. When Kate laughed I used to feel it was a horrible victory for fuse-wire and estimates over something I
couldn't actually name, but which is with one all one's life.

However, I had to start. So one evening I put all the poems, about fifty, on the table beside her and the next day hung around Kia Ora in a sort of agony. At last she appeared, but she didn't look any different or say anything. I had obviously lost. I went and had a miserable bath and was lying in the water like a man lost in an ocean. Why, I thought, couldn't things travel through the air like waves or beams? Or was life only appearance? And might one never get past that all-important frontier? When suddenly the bathroom door opened (I had forgotten to lock it) and Kate walked in.

"Oh," she said, "I'm sorry." But she didn't leave. She was laughing and suddenly she was kissing me. It was only a short kiss and then she left, still laughing, and the next day, in some way or other, I managed to push Mr. Lennox off a ladder and I was surprised to hear Kate laughing again. Kate and Mr. Lennox had a frightful row, and I knew, secretly, that I was sorry for him and all the fuses he had mended and the coops he had carpentered and the shoes he had cleaned, but I had to cross the frontier. He never came back.

The next day I asked Kate about the poems. "I haven't read all of them," she said. "Fifty is rather a lot, isn't it?" Only later she told me she hadn't read any of them. She had liked the handwriting, but it didn't matter. Finally, after ups and downs, I crossed the frontier and was amazed to discover, the next day, that everything was different only in being more the same. As time went on I sold more disinfectant, and gave up writing poems and could have become Lord Mayor of Christchurch, if it hadn't been for a man called Mr. Horner, who was the smartest dentist in town. He began to visit Kia Ora and one evening Kate told me all was over between us. A week later, after giving up disinfectant, and moping about in the garden at Kia Ora, which was full of Mr. Horner's pigeons, I decided to strike out into the bush and, if necessary, kill wild boar.

This took me a year. At that time, if not now, it was possible

17

to roam around New Zealand without a penny in one's pocket. I made for Dunedin and struck west towards the wild west coast where there was alluvial gold, paradise duck and black-widow spiders. On the way I came across most of the English public-school boys who had been with me at Wakatipu, a few like myself swagging to far horizons until they ended up in prison or were recalled home by their parents. One had become a barber's assistant in a small township in Otago; another was a barman; and the youth who had helped with the irrigation had actually married a fairly old lady in Greymouth. I helped with harvesting, worked on sheep stations, and climbed snow-topped passes. Then I returned to Christchurch.

When I reached Kia Ora, the old sweet ache gripped my bones, and I might never have gone away. I walked into the garden and found the pigeons had gone, and I could feel that Mr. Horner's presence had evaporated. I was right. Mrs. Softcup and Kate were sitting in deck chairs drinking tea; and a tall man was bending over with his back to me, pruning a rose tree. "Anthony!" cried Kate, rising. "I knew you'd be back. You look like an explorer. I want you to meet my husband. He's the new curate at St. Agnes." The tall figure turned round from the rose tree and walked towards me, hands outstretched. Flecked, magnified eyes glinted through spectacles. It was Julius Bronson, the public-school gardener from Wakatipu.

A HOT BATH AT ROTORUA

I WAS twenty and still in New Zealand. I had given up learning how to farm. I could half shear a sheep, half milk a cow, and half fell a tree. I had tried house-painting and had fallen half-way down a house. (The boss had kept me on and given me a bonus. "You keep the men happy," he had said.) So I decided to become a tourist and visit Rotorua in the North Island. I wrote to my parents, explaining that I wished to broaden my mind. "Then," I said, "I will really settle down." Eventually I received a sum of money and a letter telling me that, as far as they were concerned, my mind was now quite broad enough. I bought a ticket and a new suit and set off for Rotorua.

I had heard many fantastic things about this township, and was half expecting to see a cluster of erupting volcanoes surrounded by steam. But when I arrived I found myself in a place like Frinton-on-Sea, except that most of the neat little houses (called Sans Souci and Bide-a-Wee) had corrugated iron roofs. But there was the same atmosphere. The patter of balls on hard tennis-courts, privet hedges, whist drives, and the Rotorua Dramatic Society giving a performance of *Iolanthe*. There was a huge Victorian Thermal Establishment purveying multi-coloured baths, ranging from a sort of lemonade-

19

colour to thick pea-soup, and each of them expensively foetid. Residential hotels with old ladies in the far corner turning the pages of their Agatha Christies. Curio shops with metal kiwis and Kia Ora embroidered on mats, and Welcome to Rotorua. American tourists with cameras and fishing rods.

But after walking a short way from the town I came across a lake with steam rising all round it. I was quite alone. There was a sweet smell of sulphur and a drowsy whirr of crickets. In the distance I could hear a gurgle, a watery cough and a bang, followed by a spurt of boiling water shooting up to the sky. As I walked further round the lake, I came to places where the earth was trembling. Pits in the ground were bubbling with boiling mud, and jets of steam whistled out of rocks. It was like a gigantic, inhuman fun-fair. Its gods, faintly and shiveringly apprehended, were gods beyond known time or human experience.

Perhaps that was why the residents of Rotorua kept all these phenomena at arm's length and hardly ever referred to them, except as grotesque and mad domestic servants who only did their duty in the thermal establishments. Here, with shower baths, white-coated attendants, bath-mats and cups of tea, the terror of the gods was insulated. Of course it was different with the tourists. They wandered all over the forbidden area and the most distinguished ones even encouraged the geysers to explode, off duty, with bars of soap stuffed down their vents. They put coins in pools of water and watched them turn green. They paddled in rivers with cold water and hot bottoms, and probably didn't notice the malignant ineffable ghost crouched behind the steaming rocks. And finally they visited the Maori reservation village at Whakarewarewa.

The reservation stretches for many miles beyond Rotorua, and is inhabited by the Arawa tribe, the finest and noblest looking type of Maori. Many of them carry on the same kind of lives as other New Zealanders, and are businessmen, doctors, shopkeepers and farmers. They drive about in smart cars, wear expensive suits and smoke cigars. They play games magnificently, and read books. But there is a tacit agreement that they go to the Maori village, probably in rota, take off their suits and put on grass skirts. They plait mats, dance, and shout the thunderous Haka at illustrious visitors. There is even a Maori theatre where they enact legends, and where the dusky girls sway in the rhythm of the canoe dance.

It is a huge tourist enterprise, but by no means bogus, because the Maoris have a deep Pacific poetry in their blood, more powerful and nostalgic than all the lending libraries in New Zealand put together. The Maori place-names sing like the surf of forgotten seas and blaze like hibiscus.

I put up in a small residential hotel and began, in a rather cowardly way, to play games of tennis and fumble at bridge. I was a decent chap. I read the *Rotorua Gazette* and even had a plunge in sulphuretted hydrogen at the thermal baths. But I am not built for such solid, unperforated living, and guiltily I stole away to Whakarewarewa and spent my time hanging about the village. I met a Maori princess. She sat on the ground outside a flax-weaving hut, wearing a grass skirt and beads. She seemed highly amused. "I love sitting here and watching your people," she said, "it is such fun, and extremely educative. I simply don't need to travel. Why, an old lady gave me a peanut the other day." Later I met her at one of the hotels, dressed in a smart evening gown and drinking a cocktail. She looked just as regal. "There's a Deputation visiting the village tomorrow," she told me. "Do come. I'll be there, weaving flax."

The next day I returned to Whakarewarewa, but I didn't see any Deputation. I strolled about, talking to various friends I had made, and arrived at a small lake near a bend of the road. While I was standing there a tall naked Maori ran out of one of the huts, holding a bar of soap and a towel, threw down the towel and dived into the lake. He swam out a certain distance, lay on his back and lathered himself. Then he plunged under the water, splashed about vigorously, and swam back to the shore. He clambered out.

"That looks good," I said.

"It is good," agreed the Maori. "Try it yourself."

I felt the water with my hand. "But it's cold," I said.

"It starts cold," he said, "but you swim out and it's warm and you swim out some more and it's hot. You swim out more and it's too hot. In the middle it's boiling. No good."

"I'll have a go," I said.

He lent me his soap and towel, and I took off my clothes and jumped in.

It was cold at first, but after I had swum out a bit it felt wonderful. I splashed about in the water and lathered myself and floated in my enormous hot bath, and looked up at the sky. Then I began to swim back. At that moment I saw about thirty people lining the bank. Some of them were in uniform. One man, obviously the mayor, had a chain of office round his neck. Women were holding elaborate parasols, and somebody was making a speech. Wildly I struck back towards the centre of the lake, hit the boiling fringe, gave a shout and shot back again, treading water. The Deputation were still standing there, gazing towards me. Higher up the bank I could see a tall Maori waving and shaking with laughter.

He was wearing my suit.

⊓⊔⊓⊔⊓⊔⊓⊔⊓⊔⊓⊔⊓⊔⊓⊔⊓⊔⊓⊔⊓⊔

HOW I JOINED
THE SHEEP-SHEARERS

I WAS in Dunedin, in the South Island, selling soap. The soap was called Olo-pum. Guaranteed to remove any stains. You could clean your house with it. Dunedin is a small carbon copy of Glasgow, complete with mist. One day I decided I couldn't go on selling soap. The world was too full of wonderful things. I walked straight out of Dunedin, heading in the direction of the Haast Pass. I had heard someone mention it. It's right over the other side of the island. It's a good thing to have an objective.

I had a few shillings from my last sales of Olo-pum, and the clothes I stood up in. But once I got up into the hills above Dunedin I gave a sigh of relief. I forgot all about the soap. I felt free. I lay down in the sun for an hour or two. Then I walked west until I came to a range of mountains, which I climbed until I reached a sort of boggy plateau. At once a thick mist descended and continued until nightfall. I must have walked around in circles and it became very cold. Everywhere under my feet was bog. I was tottering with sleep.

Luckily I am the sort of person who carries masses of papers

23

about with him, old letters and bills and so on, and I decided
to make use of them. I put them on the bog and set fire to them.
This made a dry kind of mattress. I lay down on it and went to
sleep. I woke up at dawn, shivering, and went on walking. The
sole of one of my shoes began to fall off and finally succeeded,
so I went on barefoot. Suddenly a small bird flew up in front
of me and disclosed a nest with an egg in it. I ate the egg. It
was the first meal I had had since I left Dunedin.

Towards noon the mist cleared and I found a cart-track
which I followed for above five miles. This led me to a
dried-up watercourse dotted with tall trees. I was so exhausted
and hungry that I imagined the trees were talking to me, an
ancient green conversation which could only be followed in
my condition of mind. At last I came to the end of the range,
and found myself looking down into rolling green country
with a collection of homesteads in it. I immediately felt ener-
getic, stopped the green discussion, and walked down the
mountainside as fast as I could.

I knocked at the door of one of the houses, and a rather
smart man opened it. He looked at me for quite a long time,
taking me in. I don't think he had ever seen anything like me.
I was unshaven, barefoot, and black from burnt paper.

"What do you want?" he asked.

"A job," I said. "I'm on my way to the Haast Pass."

"You're hired," he said with a sudden smile. "Go to the
cookhouse."

When I turned up at the cookhouse all the men sat bolt up-
right, and one of them took out his jack-knife. The cook got
up silently and disappeared. I could hear him locking things
up. I got something to eat, but everyone was watching me like
a lynx. When I stretched out for the salt, the men's hands
jumped to their pockets. They were all waiting for a show-
down. But they didn't get it. I just got into my bunk and fell
asleep.

Three brothers ran the sheep station, and the shearing season was on. The men who had thought I was going to shoot things out were champion Australian shearers. I worked in the shed picking up the fleeces and throwing them out on the sorting table and plastering sheep-wounds with tar. The shearers called me Dead-Eye Dick, a thousand pounds reward, dead or alive. They didn't ask me where I came from. One of them made me a pair of shoes out of sacking, and another knocked up a pair of sacking trousers. I looked like a bag of potatoes, particularly because I was beginning to fill out from having seven meals a day. There was a morning snack, then breakfast, then a mid-morning snack, then lunch, then a tea-snack, followed by dinner, followed by supper. That's why shearers are so fat at the end of the season. In winter they're as thin as fencing wire.

One day one of the brothers came into the shed with a measuring tape and measured me all over. Then he asked me what size I took in boots, and wrote down all the figures in a little book. He was driving into the nearest township to fix up about sheep-sales and would get me a new outfit at the same time. Two days later was Christmas Day and I was able to wear my new clothes at a party given by the brothers. It was broiling hot, we all drank a lot of beer and played games with the children. But the next day trouble started. When I entered the cookhouse the shearers watched me out of the corners of their eyes. Again the cook rose silently and locked everything up. When I entered the shed, groups of men suddenly stopped talking. Even the sheep seemed to try to avoid me. The next day I picked up a newspaper, the *Otago Announcer*, and read an account of a desperado raiding lonely sheep stations on the Otago downs. THIS MAN IS DANGEROUS, said the headlines.

It seemed useless to try to deny that I was a desperado, since nobody had accused me. And I didn't want to talk about Olopum. The only thing to do was to play up to the part and lurch

25

about the place looking sinister. If I looked hard at the cook he backed away from me and gave me a second helping. The shearers offered me cigarettes. All the same, I felt uncomfortable. I went round to the homestead and had a talk with one of the brothers. He said, "Oh, they've caught the fellow. The *Announcer's* just arrived." He let me borrow it, and I took it around to the cookhouse in time for dinner. I read the news out aloud, but it didn't seem to make any difference. The shearers were still hostile.

We made it up later on and I discovered what the trouble was about. Cricket. England versus New Zealand. The umpire had given a wrong verdict. When the season was over I set off for the Haast Pass again.

⊔⊓⊔⊓⊔⊓⊔⊓⊔⊓⊔⊓⊔

GOING NATIVE

AFTER I had drifted to Auckland I decided to become a poet and wrote effusions for the Auckland *Trumpeter;* ten shillings a time. One day I discovered a book in the public library called *Going Native.* It was about a man who decided to leave civilisation and bury himself somewhere in the Burmese jungle with numbers of young brown wives and barrels of palm wine. It fired my imagination to such an extent that I decided to do the same.

"By all means," said the editor of the *Trumpeter,* "but we can't actually pay any money."

"But couldn't you let me have something in advance?" I asked.

"We could let you have ten shillings," said the editor; "and then, provided we liked the stories, we could send the payments to some convenient bank in the jungle."

I thanked him and immediately sent a cable to my parents in London: SETTING OFF IMPORTANT EXPEDITION BURMA NEWS- PAPER BACKING SEND MONEY URGENT. Then I waited a week in a ruined boarding-house full of coughing old men, who read books from the public library about fertility dances, vampire bats and lost races. Eventually the money arrived; I booked a berth on a ship and sailed off to Sydney.

I stayed in Sydney a week. It was full of brown parks, dry as old bones, and reminded me vaguely of a casual sort of London or New York—but for the huge, sad, patient brown trees. I went swimming on beaches which had fences to give electric shocks to sharks—the Australians have a sporting admiration for these fish. At the end of the week I got another ship to Singapore. This belonged to a Dutch line and looked very modern. I shared a small streamlined cabin with a young Australian called Bob Richards, and a Chinese gentleman, who swamped the hot air with a sharp scent of decaying lilies. Bob Richards was a reprieved murderer springing at freedom like a freed panther. He seemed to consider killing the Chinaman, but changed his mind. "If only it was a woman," he said, sniffing the terrible, flowery air. Deprived of sex for five iron years, he now planned adventures on a colossal scale with the drive and precision of a general, and had even equipped himself with a large and complicated prophylactic kit which he was glad to explain to me. "Indispensable for the islands," he said. "You should get one at the earliest opportunity." But I was still very romantic and optimistic and lacked caution, as I still do.

Most of the other passengers on the boat were enormous Australians returning to their rubber plantations and they seemed to make the ship rock. Money was thrown about in the bar like confetti. It fell to the floor and was swept up. The Australians were accompanied by plump, over-dressed wives and very pretty daughters. "Leave them alone," warned Bob. "You need a couple of copper mines." The boat, veering north, passed the Great Barrier Reef, and somewhere far out at sea a monster fish leapt into the air and exploded into the water like a bomb. I was the only person to see it. I talked about it in the bar and still talk about it. Nobody believed it. Nobody looked out to sea. The mysterious world of poets and madmen stretches far in the mind, can be touched rarely in the actual one. It bores most. At night I stood on deck with a ceiling of urgent stars and waited for something. Two days after passing the reef, I suddenly smelt the breath of flowers and turned, expecting the Chinaman. But I was alone. In the distance a bird called, clear and long; and I knew that out there was an island. Perhaps my island, the jungle of *Going Native*. I leant over the rail and was aware, sadly, that this was the nearest I should get to the East. I returned to the cabin. Bob was sharpening up his prophylactic kit, while the Chinaman knelt in the corner praying. "We'll be in Surabaya tomorrow," he said, his eyes glinting.

In the morning there was land through the porthole. It was coloured like a dream or a postcard, brilliant green palms, fire-red sampans, moon-white houses. The Australians were lined up against the deck rails, bursting with energy, shouting into the shimmering air, their women and children packed behind. It was an invasion. When we disembarked, I was suddenly swept up by ten of them, pushed through the thin streets. "Come on, boy," shouted the leader. "Rickshaws." We piled into the rickshaws and rolled into a minuscule world of gold-beaters and tiny oxen and silver bells. Men sat cross-legged outside their shops with hammers and chisels, and there was a shuddering of beaten metal and a thin scent of burning leaves. The Australians and myself looked enormous. Many of the tiny craftsmen ran into their shops and banged their doors. Women like dolls shouted "It's them," and pelted into the side streets. I couldn't get out of my rickshaw; I was British; I was huge; I was inarticulate; I desperately needed a magic potion to make myself smaller and scuttle away into the jewels and the sandalwood—the small bright chant in the hidden temple.

We drank bottles of beer and broke up brothels. Everyone and everything was running—the little flower women, the small oxen, all the strange sacred world which I was covering for the *Auckland Trumpeter*. Twice I caught a glimpse of Bob —sitting in a carriage surrounded by ten tiny women. He waved to me, and his face was shining with the light of a prophet. I thought desperately of jumping out of my rickshaw and joining him, but the pace was too fast; the angry exalted faces of the Australians shone like back-block suns; their courage and male outrage sent the insects to the sky and toppled the houses of alabaster and silk. A few hours later I was drunk; the exterior vision faded, and at some time in the night I woke up in my bunk in the Dutch ship, sniffing the old dying lilies and listening to the triumphant snore of Bob above me.

A day or two later we arrived in Singapore. Now at last I could break through the false British façade, the assumed stigma of the public school, and find my young brown wives and palm-wine barrels, and pin some sort of too-betrayed poetry, like new butterflies, on to the pages of the *Auckland Trumpeter*. But when I tried to leave the ship, I was stopped by a smart, sharp-nosed immigration officer. "You want to reside in Singapore?" he asked.

"Yes," I said.

"What is your profession?" he asked.

"Writer," I said. "I am working for the *Auckland Trumpeter*."

He seemed unimpressed. "How much money have you for your stay?"

"About two pounds ten," I said, "at this particular moment."

His mouth went thin. "In that case," he said, "you cannot possibly land."

I almost began to explain about the brown wives, and the palm-wine barrels, but decided it would be better to remain silent.

"It's no good," said the official, "you must remain in the ship until it returns to Sydney."

I stood on the deck and looked out at the harbour. Rattling up the quay in a carriage with two plumed horses was Bob, with five women throwing streamers. The Chinaman was prostrating himself at the feet of an old man with a white beard, and in the distance was a faint roar of Australians making for the bars. I went down to my cabin, took out some paper and began to write my first article for the *Auckland Trumpeter*.

THE MAN WITH THE GUN

You COULD get excited about waking up in the morning and looking at the early clouds. I had been discharged from the Dutch ship, and stood in Sydney harbour with sixpence in my pocket. I wandered about the town, fretted, mooned about in the rusty parks where the grass crackled like a burnt carpet, made absurd schemes, and finally boarded a tram. The conductor came round and asked for my fare. He had one of those slight hatchet Australian faces with a sardonic tilt to his mouth.

"Where to, chum?" he asked me.

"China," I said.

The sardonic mouth tightened, although it was perfectly true that I wanted to get to China. The Dutch ship had brought me back, ignominiously, all the way from Singapore because I hadn't had enough money to land. I had left New Zealand to penetrate China because I had read a book by a man who had turned his back on it all and married a girl called Moon Daisy. I now had the idea to work my way up to the Northern Territory, take a boat from Darwin and glide up the islands towards Malaya. All for Moon Daisy. And it really seemed quite simple.

The conductor, without altering his expression, informed me that it cost a shilling to get to the Terminus, on the edge of Sydney. "Half-way," I said, handing him my sixpence. He gave me a ticket and disappeared on his rounds. The tram clattered on, and I fell asleep. When I woke up the tram was still and the conductor was shaking my shoulder. "The Terminus," he shouted. When I had got out and was standing on the pavement he suddenly leant forward and gave me a packet. "A bit of a collection," he said. "I told them about China." The tram rattled its bell, spat some electric sparks and veered back to Sydney.

In those days Sydney ended suddenly and a primeval world tapped at your heart, the pearly gum trees guarded a million years of secret peace and a kookaburra cackled over a prehistoric joke. It was formidable, lonely, and made you long for human company. I was glad to see a car coming along the road and thumbed for a lift. The car stopped. "Come inside," cried the driver, and my Australian adventures began. At the end of the day I found myself in the Blue Mountains staying in an hotel and inspecting the waterfalls. The following day I got another lift towards the north and Moon Daisy. After about a hundred miles the driver said he was branching off east ("No good for China") and pointed towards the homestead of a cattle station a mile and a half away. I walked towards it as though across an astonishing chess set, composed of paddocks, enclosures and dairy buildings. The horizon was enormous. I could see human figures, but they were dwarfed as I felt utterly dwarfed myself. The sun shone like a stranger. I wanted to shout for assurance.

Suddenly one of the tiny white figures approached me and seemed to be running. There was a feeling of urgency. When it had reached me I saw a stout woman in a white blouse.

"Thank God you've come," she cried. "The boss has gone

off his rocker. There's only us women and old Dave and the dogs. He's been firing off his gun at us."

I tried to get the drift of this, and looked towards the peaceful-looking homestead with the smoke tapering out of the chimney.

"Where is he now?" I asked, shifting a little.

"We locked him in the woodshed," said the woman. "We'd be glad for a man in the house. We've got a good room, newly wallpapered, and the tucker's good."

"Any work I can do?" I asked in a faint voice.

"Never mind about work," said the woman. "There's old Dave and the men working out in the bush. Come along and have tea."

She tugged at my arm and drew me towards the homestead. I was very hungry and I liked the sound of the newly-papered bedroom, as long as the boss was really locked up.

An hour later I tucked into tortoise-brown chops with tomato sauce and thief-thick Australian tea brewed from the last gasp of the tea-leaf. I heard the story of the boss. His name was Edgar Robinson and he was seventy-three years old. The stout lady was his housekeeper, and she had two daughters, Lily and Rose. "Rose is a bad girl," she said. "She led poor old Edgar a hell of a dance and promised to marry him, and now she owns half the farm, two tractors, two automobiles, a pearl necklace and all the dogs. When she turned him down he ran for his gun and began shooting. Have some more chops." I accepted three more and another dense cup of black tea.

Rose and Lily joined us at the table. They were both pretty, but Lily was rather thin and glum. Rose had a gypsy face, merry as a hawthorn, and never stopped laughing about Edgar. "False teeth and a metal stomach," she said, crunching her chop. "Why don't you go and see him? Knock at the wood-shed door. Here's the key." Her mother expostulated, but Rose kept looking at me with a dare in her eye. I took the key and walked out of the cookhouse towards the woodshed. I stood there for a few minutes and then knocked.

"Who is it?" asked a frail, educated voice behind the door.

"Me," I said.

"Who are you?"

"An Englishman," I said.

"What are you doing here?" asked the voice.

"I am going to China," I said.

There was a fairly long pause.

"May I come and see you?" I said.

"By all means," replied the voice.

I turned the key in the lock, opened the door slowly and peered into the shed. Under the light of a naked bulb a long, thin man was lying on a pile of sacking reading a book. Beside him lay a gun.

"Forgive me for not rising," he said, waving his hand. "The name is Robinson."

"Mine is Carson," I said.

I sat down on the floor beside him, and suddenly we were talking about Naples. He had never been there, but he seemed to have an extraordinary interest in Vesuvius.

"Does it smoke like a cigar?" he asked me.

"Like a beautiful cigar," I said.

"How lucky you are to have seen it," he said. "You are only a young man, but you have something rich to remember. It gets very lonely here, you know."

"Do you want to come back to the house?" I asked, making a tentative gesture towards the gun.

"No," he shouted suddenly, and then his voice softened. "Thank you for the talk about Vesuvius. Remember, young man, it is only too easy to forget about things like that. Lock the door on the outside. Goodbye."

35

"Goodbye," I said, and locked the door.

I stayed in the house four more days. They had let the old man out and he seemed quite peaceful. I left for the north and Moon Daisy. Lily had given me a little white dog called Spin. As I got back on to the road I thought I heard two shots ring out.

⎍⎍⎍⎍⎍⎍⎍⎍⎍⎍

A FORTNIGHT WITH CEMENT

I WAS swagging my way up to the Northern Territory. Swagging is an honourable profession in Australia and an arduous one. The country is enormous, thirsty and primeval. There can be days of monotonous brown earth, and gum trees, without sight of human life, and only a host of fantastic preoccupied animals and birds to keep one company. They scream, whistle, jump, juggle and creep like no animals anywhere else, and they drag you back into the lyrical timelessness of prehistory. That is why Australian bushwhackers have that strange far-away look in their eyes—they have been right off the map. Morning after morning I woke up staring into the hysterically inquisitive eyes of an emu, and on one occasion, in Queensland, I strolled for ten minutes with an enormous lizard, seven feet long, which eventually climbed a tree. I was glad of its company.

The sheep and cattle stations welcome swagmen, and are glad of their visits. A dozen empty chairs wait for them in the cookhouse, and in the morning they get a hand-out of flour, bacon, tea, meat and sugar. The Australian swagman, unlike his English counterpart (and I have slept in casual wards), is incredibly optimistic and talks about undiscovered

37

goldfields, forests of precious timber, fruit and well-paid work. It is always further on, another thousand miles, but it is an enormous country and he may find it. He is blackened by sun, contorted by thirst, and stamped with the unearthly monotony of endless horizons. The stations themselves are populated by eccentrics, particularly with fencers who may live a month among nothing but sheep and end up by talking to them. I met one in New South Wales who put lumps of earth in his drinking water. Raspberry jam sent him mad, and he had invented a dog language. It took three months back at the homestead to put him right.

I had many adventures and was becoming absorbed by the vast, beautiful thoughtlessness of the parched land, when I arrived in a small township in Queensland without money but with an enormous thirst. Someone told me that there was a job going. Cementing tanks. But that was not all. The tank-cementer must be able to bake damper. "Damper" is an Australian specialty. It is bread made in an iron pot over a wood fire, and it has to be baked according to a certain recipe, heat and timing. Recklessly I applied for the job. My employer was a short, wiry man with an efficient face, who, I felt at once, was an expert on tank-cementing and the exactitudes of damper. "I can't bake the stuff myself," he said, "but I know just how it should be. It's very important that it should be exactly right. Particularly when you mix cement out there where we're going. Damper is the only thing to look forward to." I felt very uneasy about this, because I had never mixed cement or baked damper in my life. But he hired me, and we set off in his battered lorry for the tank country.

This proved to be the most arid place I had yet struck, an inferno of hard red earth dotted with a few sickly gum trees and watered by a small pallid lagoon covered with scum. The tanks were colossal and radiated the semi-tropical heat of the sun. Turn by turn we drove off to a sandpit, loaded up, and drove back. Then we mixed the cement inside the huge oven of the tank until I began to feel like stewed steak. After two sweltering hours my employer cocked an eye on me. "Better get to work on the damper," he said.

"Right," I said.

I nipped out of the tank and made a fire. That part was simple. Then I took the top off the iron pot, mixed some flour, water and baking powder, and pounded it into a chaotic, entangling, octopus-like mass whose tentacles clung round my arms and worked up towards my hair.

While I was battling with it there was a cry from the tank.

"How you doing?" cried Bill, my employer.

"Fine," I cried back, pushing most of the hostile mess into the pot and replacing the lid. Half an hour later Bill climbed out of the tank, white from head to foot. I could only see his eyes.

"Let's get at that damper," he said.

I opened the lid and took out something grey and shapeless. It smelt vaguely of cork.

"Here we are," I said faintly.

Bill sliced it with his knife and smelt it, then slid it into his mouth.

"Too much baking powder got in," I said.

He didn't look at me.

In the evening we had a wash, which meant jumping into the tepid lagoon and splashing about. I couldn't actually feel the water because we were covered with layers of cement which grew thicker and thicker as time went on. Water wouldn't take it off, it merely turned the cement into a kind of slime which hardened stiff in the sun until we were two pterodactyls in the wilderness. During this ineffectual bath the damper was cooking. The second day it was burnt black, and the third the fire went out. On the fourth day Bill approached me in the tank.

39

"You can't cook damper," he said, spitting out some cement.

"No," I confessed, "but I'll learn."

"You're not so good on the cement either," he said, "but it wouldn't have mattered if you'd have been good at damper. That's why I hired you."

He went away and came back ten minutes later. "It's a fair cow," he said. This is Australian for being in a hopeless situation. He didn't speak to me for the rest of the fortnight. Side by side, tormented by flies, we sweated in the tank, and splashed in the lagon. Side by side we ate grisly damper which turned up, every day in a new form, lymphatic, rigid, porous, semi-combustible. Then he paid me off and I went to the nearest township. I had a throat like a lime kiln. I drank very seriously for a whole day, and came to with my hair cut and shampooed, my face massaged and my shoes polished. Then I went to have dinner.

"I'm sorry," said the waiter, "but no bread has been delivered. We only have damper."

"Bring some cement too," I said.

The waiter nodded his head with the special indulgence one accords to drunks.

Lᴦᴸᴦᴸᴦᴸᴦᴸᴦᴸᴦᴸᴦ

HOW I NEARLY BECAME A STAR

I LEFT Australia and came back to England, smelling slightly
of sheep, and gazed with utter bewilderment at the dying
Twenties. People were being terribly bitter, terribly gay,
terribly clever, and I didn't know what it was all about. I had
been with too many horses and Australia is too empty and
enormous to have such subtle significances. My brother was
bang in the middle of it, bitter, gay and clever, and he tried to
incorporate me into the savage tinsel, but soon he came to the
conclusion that I didn't fit. It was like trying to introduce a
kangaroo into a Kensington nightclub.

My family had lost most of their money in the Wall Street
slump, so it wasn't possible to send me back. However, after
trying to be bitter, gay and clever, and not finding any suitable
work ("You should go back to the Colonies"), I bought a bicycle, shipped it on to St. Malo and began to bicycle to Spain.
My allowance was ten shillings a week. I had a sleeping-bag
and cooking equipment, and bought simple food as I went
along. When I reached the Spanish frontier a hot barbaric
wind blew in my face, there was a distant sound of drums and
a smell of crude olive oil. I have never forgotten it since. By
the time I reached Madrid I heard there was a revolution.

"Where is the revolution?" I asked in village after village. "Further south," they said, pointing. One morning I knew I had arrived in the South. The buildings looped, the arches curved, the cats and dogs were all asleep, and the girls were singing like fairies by the fountain. I entered an inn and waited hours for lunch, swallowing flies. Finally a lovely slattern came in and threw bread, wine and a dreadful omelet on the table.

"Where's the revolution?" I asked.

"We've had it," the lovely slattern cried proudly. "All my brothers were in it and they shot people. It was like a feast day. Now it is further south."

I never really came across the revolution, except possibly when a very courteous man was showing me around a cathedral. "Here is the exquisite rose window," he said, "and this is a perfect Gothic arch. Note the plateresque on the walls and the Murillo over the altar." When we walked outside the church I could see flames coming out of the roof.

"But the church is on fire," I cried.

"That has nothing to do with me," said my guide. "I wish to show you our amazing cemetery."

After visiting the Feria in Seville I made north again and pedalled for France. There were a few adventures. I was arrested, released, and discovered a cave colony of dwarfs near Valencia. I never saw the dwarfs but found a minute donkey in a miniature chalk manger chewing hay. Once over the frontier I made for Nice. I decided to stay there.

This meant looking for work. But it was not easy to find. One day, sun-bathing on the beach, I met a film director who offered me a small part in a film about Arabs. "Silly-ass role," he said. "Topee, eye-glass and cigar." I went to the studio, was made up and given some dialogue. "Jolly decent show, old bean, what?" was what I was asked to contribute to the Arab film. It was only the kind-heartedness of the director. For three weeks afterwards I kept turning up as a camel-attendant, my face blacked by cocoa. "Keep away from the camera," said the film director, "you'll last till the end of the film." After that I was a gardener, a gendarme, and a corpse. I collected my money and wandered away to Juan-les-Pins, where I became a swimming instructor to an extremely smart yacht club. It was a pleasant enough life until, with the barbarity of fate, I developed terrible toothache and had to remove myself to Nice.

I was back on the beach. The sun shone, the sea glittered, and life was a long open book without any definable prospect. I drifted to the Russians and fell impossibly in love with a beautiful young girl called Ekaterina Nina Popolski. She always sat beside me knitting.

"For whom are you knitting?" I would ask.

"He is far away," she would reply, and give a deep sigh.

I would try to tell her about my ambitions, but she always seemed buried in her knitting, her delicious face obscured by wool.

"Life is sad," she would say, "but we must be grateful for the sun shining and the waves playing."

"You are very beautiful," I would say.

"Alas," she replied.

The woollen garments grew longer and longer, and I terribly wanted to eat. She had many brothers who gave me soup, and I am sure they felt very sorry for me. I met Grand Dukes and Archdukes and Princes and Barons and Generals, some of whom drove taxis up and down the Promende des Anglais or waited on millionaires in the grand hotels, and I met other Russian girls, but none as beautiful as Ekaterina Nina Popolski. Finally her wool ran out and she actually kissed me. I moved to another part of the beach, near an establishment called the Grand Bleu.

It was here that I met Gloria. She was a blonde nearly-young American woman of such dynamism that the tideless waves struggled to get farther up the beach. She was surrounded by a group of men whom I knew to be, like myself, the flotsam of Nice, cast up, for one reason or another, on this brittle shore of chancy pleasure. There were a couple of drunkards, a drugged remittance man and a few unemployables, besides a number of strikingly pretty girls who, in those far-off times, used to turn up in any nook or cranny of the Riviera to sift possibilities. Gloria Raven had been married about five times, but, like so many American women, had lost none of her enthusiasm. "I just love men," she said to me simply, "but I have a greater love and that is the theatre." She explained to me that she was launching an Anglo-French repertory company, and that all the people sitting around her trembling in the suburbs of delirium tremens constituted her company. "Anybody is potential," she said, looking at me with her elemental blaze. "Anybody is a great natural actor. Anybody is a potential liver who can integrate himself with the great give-and-take of existence. Join us. Fame may be around the corner."

"I will join you," I said. "Is there any chance of a sandwich?"

As it was, we lived on sandwiches while we rehearsed *The Ideal Husband*. Gloria's production technique was founded on her deep sexual experience and modern American theatre workshop innovations. "Go back behind the lines," she cried. "Lines don't matter. Start acting five minutes before your entrance cue. Take an imaginary bath, an imaginary taxi, and never stop thinking sex. Sex, sex, sex, it's there behind all the dialogue, thank God." In no time at all she had the dipsomaniacs trembling like whipped dogs, and the pretty girls crying through the curtains of their pale lusts. "You all need aphrodisiacs," she cried. Whenever there was a love scene she jumped up and down in the auditorium. "Mean it," she

44

shouted. "Go away and mean it and then come back." But there were not enough sandwiches. So Gloria met some millionaires and impresarios and managed to hire the Méditerranée for one night. Her energy was astounding. In some way we all came to life, and we thought back behind the lines, and meant sex, and actually gave a performance which was reported in the *Eclaireur de Nice*. "Very tasteful indeed," it said. "A perfect example of gentlemanly control."

The next day we were called for a conference. Some of us had managed to acquire rather terrible new suits, and there was the sign of hair-cuts and regeneration. But, except for the pretty girls, we were quite a dreadful crew. "We are all going to Paris," said Gloria, who had suddenly acquired a fur coat and a Long Island look. "I have met someone who is interested in starting an Anglo-French dramatic centre. We will have our own theatre, club and so on, and hold conferences and art exhibitions."

We travelled to Paris the next day and stayed in tiny insanitary hotels, four to a room. The sandwiches seemed smaller than the ones in Nice, and it was much colder. Nobody believed any more in the theatre, and we had half-hearted rehearsals in a large gloomy café near the Gare St. Lazare. One by one the Riviera tramps drifted away, and the pretty girls gravitated towards the Bois. Then, to the amazement of us who remained, Gloria discovered a theatre near the Odeon. It was a small theatre like a charming invalid at death's door. But its heart had not stopped beating. Gloria was radiant, jumping up and down off the stage, trying the curtains, declaiming for acoustics. "Very few of the company remain with us," she said, "so I propose that we perform a piece called *Le Salaud*, by Verneuil. There are only three characters, and I will get it translated into English immediately." The three people cast for the play were a man called Laurence Noland, an ageing lady from Boston who was providing Gloria with cheques, and myself. Laurence Noland was one of those eccentric Englishmen who floated through Europe like a smart balloon waiting to be attached to something. Gloria's forcefulness acted on him like the sun with a dew-drop. He dissolved and became her slave, threw away his bowler hat and umbrella, and thought back hours behind his opening lines.

"You have as much sex as an asparagus," Gloria would shout from the auditorium.

"I'm terribly sorry," Mr. Noland would answer in cultured tones. "I'll try again."

When the piece came on there was an amazingly fashionable audience whom Gloria had netted at cocktail parties and in the smarter bars. "Throw all the sex into it you've got, boys," cried Gloria at the dressing-room door. When the curtain went up Noland and I were both chattering with nerves, and the leading lady looked as old as a Coptic parchment. At the end of the play there was discreet applause, and Gloria made a long speech hypnotising the audience. The next morning I was summoned to her hotel. She was glowing like a coal. "Success," she cried. "You'll never look back. Have you ever heard of Marie Janel?" I had. She was one of France's leading actresses. "Marie Janel has consented to appear with you and Laurence at the next performance. She is bilingual, and wants to practise her English."

"But what about the old lady?" I asked.

"She died last night," said Gloria gaily. "She had a fit in her dressing-room. Now, pay attention. Marie Janel wants you to go and see her at her house this morning for a run-over. Don't forget all I've told you."

I rang the bell at Marie Janel's apartment. A beautiful girl opened the door with a welcoming smile.

"Mademoiselle Janel," I cried, "this is such an honour."

"I am the maid," replied the girl modestly, showing me into the drawing-room.

46

When Marie Janel finally entered the room I could feel the invisible wings of success winnowing at my ears, I could sense the rush of high-powered cars, the lure of expensive perfumes, the chic chatter of wonderful restaurants, endless applause and all the fashionable quarters of love.

The same afternoon I called at the theatre to find Gloria. I met Laurence Noland standing in the vestibule unbelievably crying.

"I am sorry to behave like this," he said fatuously, taking out a silk handkerchief and blowing his nose, "but the theatre's being dismantled."

"Dismantled!" I shouted.

"Yes. And Gloria is in prison. Something to do with cheques."

"Whose cheques?" I cried.

"The old lady's," said Noland miserably. "The one who died. She had no money at all."

We stood looking at the doomed theatre, listening to the muffled sound of hammers and saws. It was suddenly very cold.

"Come and have some lunch," said Noland at last. "But I can only afford sandwiches."

THE BANDIT

DURING that first time I bicycled to Spain I raced the dying winter to Perpignan. At the Spanish frontier the drums of spring already sounded, and a wind from Africa, hot as a fabulous brothel, blew through the customs shed. Further and further south I went. "Seville?" I cried to people on the road. "Seville," they cried back, pointing, and slowly I reached young leaves and the cool swoop of arches and time sleeping like a dog in the sun. Then I climbed a hill, and orange blossom, like a perfume of ancient empires, was in the breeze. I saw an old man scratching the soil with a hoe. "Seville?" I shouted. "Seville," he cried back, and suddenly, as though he knew the urgency, took me by the hand and ran with me to the top of a hill and I looked down. Seville lay below me like an exquisite ivory chess set. Two years later I returned to Seville, and stayed in a derelict inn across the Guadalquivir. In the distance I could see the elegant finger of the Giralda point to the sky. The inn was kept by a retired bullfighter, who had three sons, Luis, Pedro and Miguel. Luis and Miguel were bullfighters, Pedro was a footballer. "Praise be to God!" said his mother. Pedro had bulging calves and knew everything about English cup-ties. "To fight bulls is not a thing of education," he told me. Though Luis and Miguel lacked the modern education of the bull, they had more charm. Particularly Miguel. Miguel was a very young man who was just beginning to fight terrible old bulls in obscure villages.

"They know Latin and Greek," he told me, "and are as big as cathedrals."

He was keen on his art, and used to practise cloak and muleta with a wild boar, called the Bandit, which he kept chained up to an olive tree near the inn. The Bandit was growing a fine pair of tusks and ripped Miguel's trousers to ribbons as he practised with a half-veronica and went in for the kill with a wooden sword. In the evenings, when the inn was crammed with gossips, Miguel unchained the Bandit and it wandered in through the door and rooted among the tables. Everyone screamed and jumped up on chairs, devout old women prayed to various regional Virgins, and manzanilla and anis ran all over the floor.

One day Miguel came into my room, which was crammed with a lot of rather bored canaries, and said, "Tomorrow we go to the carnival. You must get yourself a typical costume and we will hire a carriage and join the procession." I borrowed a black Cordoba hat, a white waistcoat and stove-pipe trousers. "We wear masks," said Miguel, "and speak in high falsetto. Nobody speaks in their own voice during the carnival." The next day we got into the carriage, and there were two gypsy girls in it called Consolation and Conception, and we joined a stream of other carnival carriages and screamed at each other in falsetto voices and posed as typically as possible. For about an hour the carnival was a gracious, quite elegant affair, and people screamed and threw flowers at the carriages, but later on everyone got drunk and they started throwing earth and I lost my hat and Miguel bashed a man over the head with a guitar. "This is a good carnival," screamed Miguel. "Now we'll get out of the carriage and walk down the street and sweep everyone off the pavement. Consolation and Conception, walk behind us." We did this and later found ourselves in a cake shop near the Sierpes. "I must go," said Miguel, "and feed the Bandit." After he had left, some young men came in and screamed at us and we threw cakes at each other, while the proprietor bowed and jotted down each item on a bill. After the cake fight was over one of the young men waved magnificently and left.

"The Marquis is paying," said the proprietor with another bow. "He never misses the carnival cake fight, does the Marquis. A proper young señorito."

When I returned to the inn, covered with cream, it was night and the fish were leaping like knives in the river. I started to make for my room, when I heard a terrible snuffling and froze where I stood. "Keep still," cried the voice of Miguel, now deep and natural. "Don't move an inch. He will probably only sniff at you. Behave like a tree." I listened to the snorting approach of the Bandit and behaved like a tree, though a trembling one. It zigzagged through the night and nosed to my feet, suspicious and bristling. After ten minutes of toppling terror I heard it lunge away and I tiptoed to my room, and collapsed into the bed.

Later I left Spain, and Miguel saw me off at the station.

"You will come back to Seville," he shouted.

"I will come back," I shouted back.

"For the carnival," shouted Miguel in a suddenly high voice.

"For the carnival," I screamed back in falsetto, and the train left and I tried never to let the magic go; but it went, petering out among prams and privet and red brick crescents in the rain.

Twenty years later, grey and not so near the stars, I found myself back in Seville. I got myself a carriage and drove through the old flower-studded streets, the barrio of Santa

Cruz, the Alcazar, and then across the river to the inn of my honeymoon. A plump woman served me with a manzanilla. She looked at me with curiosity and said suddenly, "You are the man in the photograph?" She pointed to a glass case which contained pictures of bullfighters, and in the very centre a photograph of Miguel, myself, Conception, Consolation and El Sordo driving away for the carnival. I sat down and drank many manzanillas, and the Giralda glittered in the distance like a vision. The woman was Pedro's wife. "His father and mother are dead and so are Luis and Pedro. Miguel will be here this evening. I will tell him you are here."

I returned in the evening. It was already dark and I paused at the broken-down gate of the inn. In the distance I could hear the tinkle and rumble of a guitar, and it woke a sleeping nerve. I walked forward and suddenly froze. Something was snuffling and snorting under the trees. I stood absolutely still for twenty minutes and then, as the creature got closer, I shouted "Miguel!"

All the lights of the inn went on, and a tall dark man came running out, laughing, to embrace me. A little way away, staring up at me with minute, suspicious eyes, was a tiny pig.

THE DUCE AT HOME

WAR WAS blowing up. I arrived in Rome. I was wearing a new
suit made by a tailor in a tiny Italian village who had copied
it from an old American magazine. It was quite smart, with
huge shoulders, but it had suddenly begun to bristle with
horsehair. I stayed in a small hotel and visited people to whom
I had introductions. There was a marchesa from Brooklyn,
someone in the Vatican, an aged essayist who was already beginning to attack the West, and a millionairess who appeared
at dinner covered with old gold. It was at her house that I met
two Poles. One was short and fat and the other tall and thin,
both with busy diplomatic mouths and secrets in their eyes.
The short one was called Stanislaus Oman and the other Fedor Prim. It was during coffee that the talk turned to films
and both Stanislaus and Fedor discussed long shots and back
projection.

"Are you working in films?" I asked the short Pole.

The golden millionairess broke out in a laugh. "Why," she
said, "don't you know? I thought everyone knew. These gentlemen have come here to make a film about the Duce."

The next day I happened to meet them again in the street,
and they invited me to have some coffee. We talked about

films, and, since I urgently wanted to find some money, I mentioned that I had worked on films myself.

"Splendid," said Fedor. "In what capacity?"

"Scripts," I said.

"Excellent," agreed Stanislaus. "Good writers are welcomed here in Cinecittà. Perhaps you would care to accompany us when we visit the State Director of Cinematography this afternoon?"

"I should be delighted," I said.

That afternoon I met them outside a large building patrolled by armed guards. We were formally searched by smiling police and then allowed to ascend in a magnificent lift to the Director's office. We knocked at the door and, when it opened, were passed by two detectives into a large, sumptuous room with a huge desk at the end of it. Behind it sat a large, powerful man with a hooked nose. He rose, smiling. He was dressed in some sort of smart white uniform with gold braid; it was difficult to say whether it was naval or military. We sat in elegant chairs and were given cigarettes. A moment later the door opened, and a very fat man in a light-blue uniform, jangling spurs, entered the room, saluted the Director, placed some photographs on his desk, saluted again and left. The Director glanced at the photographs, and from where I was sitting I could see they were nudes. "That is one of our leading directors," he explained, putting the photographs away in a drawer.

The Poles' proposed film about the Duce dealt with his domestic life, wife, children and pets (dogs, cat and canary) and was set in the kitchen, the garden, the bathroom, nursery and scullery. The Duce would appear in shirt-sleeves, dressing-gown, old suit, move about with gardening gear, feed the canary or cat, water the flowers, play at toy trains with the children, and one would even watch him eating spaghetti and drinking a tumbler of Chianti.

"You will be glad to know that the Duce has approved of the idea," said the State Director. "He likes the simplicity of it, and the presentation of himself to his people as the simple, homely, family man he indeed is."

"Exactly," said Prim. "It will lead to understanding among nations, and will help to remove the threat of war."

I felt that it was time to leave, as business would now be discussed. I rose and the State Director rose.

"You are in films?" he asked me.

"Mr. Carson is very well known in the English film world," said Prim. "Perhaps he might be useful to you."

"I will bear it in mind," said the Director, and I could see that he was staring at my coat with some intensity.

A week later I landed a job in the British Library. It was directed by a large woman with the face of a Roman Emperor, and her name was Mrs. Wetherby. She had lived twenty years in Rome and gave enormous archaeological tea-parties. War or no war, she was as immovable as the Colosseum, and she would only leave Rome if every brick of the city went with her. I handed out volumes of *Rambles in the Campagna*, *A Paint Brush at the Villa d'Este*, Riskin, and novels by Warwick Deeping and Dornford Yates. I also dusted copies of the *Illustrated London News*. On Fridays I went to the archaeological tea-parties, and since there was no more horsehair left in my suit I wore a thick black coat which had belonged to an old antiquarian who had suddenly died in Mrs. Wetherby's house.

At these parties I met most of the people to whom I had been given introductions, the American marchesa, the Vatican official, the aged essayist and the millionairess. The last, who was a widow and had two daughters at Roedean, fearful of the fate of her money, had suddenly become much enamoured of the State Director of Cinematography. Mrs. Wetherby shrugged her shoulders about this and poured a hundred cups of tea as a libation to the old Gods who always, in Rome, whispered around the corner. Finally I came across the two Poles, Stanislaus Oman and Fedor Prim, and it was evident that everybody knew about their film, although discussion was polite and formal. Secretly, Roman society considered the Duce a rather outrageous joke, an idealisation of shopkeepers, and behind the closed doors of their palaces they roared with marble laughter.

I went on working at the British Library, and Rome was beginning to bulge with generals and admirals swooping through the streets in armoured cars and the streets were thick with German tourists on coal-ticket exchange. They moved about with vouchers, gave no tips, and were unpopular. Some of my Italian friends wept, the easels and the folios abandoned, the Villa d'Este a plague of cola tickets, the factories smoking with death on instalment. The Gods had gone, the Virgins mourned and the marble laughter was still.

But Mrs. Wetherby carried on with her tea-parties, and although the attendance was smaller, there was still tattle of Claudius and Michelangelo and poor Hadrian. And then one day the announcement was made. The film about the Duce had been completed. It would be exhibited to the élite of Rome by special invitation, and would be attended by members of all the armed forces. The film was entitled *The Duce at Home*. Naturally Mrs. Wetherby was invited, and she insisted that I should go as well. "As a member of the British Library," she said.

"But I have no clothes to go in," I said.

"That can be arranged," she said. "The late antiquary left some sort of evening suit."

She fetched it for me. It was green, and had a label which stated that it was made in Buenos Aires in 1890.

"Very distinguished and oddly Roman," said Mrs. Wetherby.

The night arrived, and when we reached the theatre there was a sea of people, police, photographers and a blinding gilter of uniforms and medals and jewels. A whisper was going round that the Pope would arrive, but Mrs. Wetherby put this down to hysteria or Communist agitators. We went into the theatre and found our seats, waved to acquaintances and the amplifiers boomed with *Giovinezza*. Suddenly there was a sort of hurricane of escaping breath and everybody turned, and there at the back, on a sort of dais, was the Duce. Then the lights were lowered and the film began. *The Duce at Home*, directed and photographed by Stanislaus Oman and Fedor Prim.

It opened with a long shot of Mussolini walking down the street carrying a brief-case. He might have been a business man returning from a conference. He arrived at his door, where he was greeted by his wife. "It has been a tiring day," said the sound-track. His wife took his hat and brief-case, and later we saw the Duce in shirt-sleeves walking into the garden and mowing the lawn. "Nature gives relaxation," said the sound-track. A dog arrived, and he patted it and gave it a biscuit. Then he patted a child on the head and played with the cat. "A lover of animals," said the sound-track, and then, when the Duce entered the kitchen and sat down, the sound-track made some remark about the inner man. It was when he actually began eating spaghetti that the first giggle spiralled into the air, and it joined another giggle, and then there were giggles weaving into each other all over the theatre, and these formed a trickle of laughter, and then a gurgle of laughter and then a huge waterfall of laughter. I was surprised to see Mrs. Wetherby sobbing helplessly into her handkerchief. Suddenly the film stopped, the lights went on, and there was a long agony of utter silence. No one dared to look behind him, and in the same burden of silence everyone trooped out of the theatre and into the street.

A few weeks later I returned to England and tried to pick up the strands of a disconnected life, severed when I had left London for a weekend in Paris which had lasted three years. One day, glancing at an evening paper, I saw a small news item. "Poles shot near Italian frontier," it said, and continued: "Two Poles were shot trying to cross from the Italian frontier yesterday. They were said to be carrying films of secret plans stolen from the Ministry of War in Rome, and were named as British secret agents."

But it might have been two other Poles.

THE GIRL FROM BARCELONA

I CAME BACK from Italy to Paris. I knew Inge would be at
the station. And there she was, and I hugged her and said
things in Spanish.

"You've got an Italian accent," she said angrily.

"I can't help it," I said.

It was true, there was a false, singing note. Spanish is hard,
moon-white, hammered out for any kind of truth. Italian is
like rotten fruit, gay and dangerous with wasps. It was really
more like me. I went back to French and then to English. I
am not really good at languages, I am not a monkey.

"What are you going to do?" asked Inge.

"Write a book," said I, which was an easy thing to say in
the drama of the station: there it was, neat, shining and clear in
my mind, pages effortlessly filled, a mirror of my days.

I had met Inge a month before I had left for Italy, at a party
given in Montparnasse by an American opera-singer called
Hilda. At this party were the cream of the collectors, the collected and the half-way people who paid for the drinks and
incidental flourishes, the people who visit the exhibitions, read
the books, say the things, but are really always sound-proof.
"This is the girl," said Hilda, introducing me to Inge. She

looked quite simple, radiant and modest, but was dry and brittle as an unwatered flower bed. She was a nurse in the Civil War, had been in prison on both sides, and was now given leave of absence to rest in Paris.

Always the beginning of a love-affair has the music of spring, and at once the houses of Paris settled down in their luminous places, and the minute things like bread, buses and grocers' shops glowed with a light of eternity. First there was the hotel by the Tuileries, the confessions, the absolution, and the gay breakfast; and then we went to stay in the house of her uncles and cousins. To my surprise these turned out to be Jews from Berlin, small and gentle; and we talked about literature (since I had adopted for myself the title of "author" in the brilliant, shiftless circus of Montparnasse).

Then one day Inge told me she had to leave Paris for a short time, but that she would be back and that I was not to worry. She refused to explain why, and in some way I imagined I should never see her again. I tried to write my book (something formless about New Zealand) but the shape of phrases eluded me; I was obsessed by the magic of loving; I was hungry for present triumph among the world's flowers. Somewhere, behind the summer in the cafés, stood the huge dull monster of war tearing up the petals and starting to shoot the birds. And I hadn't lived. At last Inge returned. The streets of Paris shone again, but she steadfastly refused to say where she had been.

We went to live in the forest of Rambouillet. At first we stayed in a strange dusty inn at Celles les Bordes, where there was a mechanical piano made in 1906. In the morning it was surrounded by poultry, the sun plunged in, and we danced for hours. Madame, who had ringworm, sat on the floor peeling potatoes and shelling peas. "Dance, my children," she cried. "Dance while you can." We were the only guests. Once she pointed out of one of the opaque windows at a small brown

59

house. "This is quite a famous village," she said proudly. "That was where Landru was born." There was also a sort of composite shop, which sold bootlaces, sausages, cough-mixture, fishing-rods and postcards of lovers among the cherry blossom.

In the afternoons we walked through the forest, thick with the hot smell of fern, and we nearly always went towards the bean fields. Inge had a wild hunger for beans.

"Why beans?" I asked her.

"In Spain there are sometimes only beans in the battlefields," she said.

She sat on the ground, shelling beans, and singing Republican songs; and she was hardly there, beside me, in the French forest at all.

"Where do you go when you go away?" I asked her.

"I will tell you one day," she said.

One day Hilda arrived at the hotel with a rich lover, a Swiss banker; and we sat downstairs drinking their red wine. There was a tune on the mechanical piano from *Manon*; we played it and Hilda began singing. She sang to us and the poultry and to Landru's house and the spiders on the ceiling. Life was a summer afternoon's dream.

We moved to Clairefontaine and found an absurd small house in the forest about a mile away from the village. The front of the house was covered with rambling roses. It had electric light, a small kitchen and a garden the size of a towel, with ten radish plants and some celery and a few poppies. It had obviously been built for a dwarf married couple, or a mountain bourgeois with a Japanese mistress, or perhaps an old lonely man who loved birds not too far from Paris. We stayed there for about a week, and then Inge told me that she had to go away in a few days.

"For God's sake, why?" I cried.

"I have to, for a number of reasons," she said. "Perhaps the main, obvious reason is that we have no more money. You have to write your book."

"I don't," I said. "Tell me where you are going," I asked. I felt insane and jealous. I didn't want the forest without her.

"I will tell you when I come back," she said.

The next day Hilda and her Swiss banker came to visit us. They had brought some champagne and we had a picnic in front of the house. Hilda sang again. She sang with a free golden heart but with economy. Hers was a very neat life. They packed up the picnic baskets, drove off to Paris, and left us alone in the darkening forest. In two days Inge would go. We were both wanderers, each of us almost without countries; but I knew that she was the stronger and the clearer of us. I told her so while we sat drinking coffee on the bed. She decided then to tell me about where she was going.

"It's to the Spanish frontier," she said.

"Why the frontier?" I said.

"Because I meet a man there."

"How do you know he'll be there?" I asked with a sick feeling.

"Because it's an arrangement," she said.

There was a pause.

"Who is he?" I asked.

"He's a man with Franco," she said.

"But you are not with Franco."

"Certainly not," she said. "I am from Catalonia, I am with the Republic. I met this man in one of the prisons."

"Which side?" I asked.

"It doesn't matter which side," she said. "I had been helping to carry in pilots who had crashed near Barcelona. Most of them were charred. I was captured and stayed in this prison for about six months. One day I went to a window and began to jump out to kill myself but someone stopped me. It was this man."

"And who is he?"

"He's an important man with Franco. He is a colonel. But he is not a politician. He is simply someone; the sort of person you can find only in Spain, in the middle of a Civil War, who is as noble and great as Spain itself."

There was another pause, and I tried to think and understand.

"And he comes to meet you?"

"Certainly," she said.

"Is it dangerous?"

"Of course," she said, "but he is always there. We meet in the mountains. He brings me money and messages from my mother."

It was now quite dark and an owl hooted.

"When are you leaving?" I asked.

"Tomorrow," she said.

In the morning she packed her knapsack, and we walked together to the cool fringe of the road. "Goodbye," she said. She looked at me, and I remembered her as she sat, fancy free, singing in the bean field. "You can get credit in the inn," she said. "I will be back soon." She walked away down the road; and then she suddenly came back. "There is no love-making," she said, "it is out of the question."

I stayed in the minute Japanese bird-house for two days, completely motiveless. The music had stopped, and I had no inner music to compose. This was the time to construct a fortress from the intermittent, slowly receding rivers of life, but I did no such thing. At the end of the second day huge clouds began to cover the sky and the forest was utterly black. Rain began to fall, and I retreated into the doll's house. An hour later there was an enormous crash of thunder, a stab of lightning, and the lights of the house fused. There was nothing to see but the night, nothing to hear but the rain. In the morning it was clear and fine again, and the fuses were mended. I waited another week. And then for another. But Inge never appeared.

One morning I was woken up by a voice singing. It was a piece from *Manon* that we had played on the mechanical piano in Celles les Bordes. I looked out through the roses to see Hilda and the banker with a picnic basket.

"Where's Inge?" shouted Hilda.

"I don't know," I said. "I don't know."

I never saw her again. A man I knew in Paris called Faraday gave me a return ticket to London (which somebody didn't want because of a horizon of love; and there I was, standing in Newhaven harbour.

"British?" said a huge policeman.

"Yes," I said.

"On the right," said the policeman.

HOME CHAT

I WAS out of the army. For want of something better to do, I used to walk round and round the pond in Kensington Gardens in the company of a tall, thin, bending man called Sandiman. Buds appeared, dogs barked, model boats hooted, kites flew up, leaves shimmered, the band played, leaves dropped and the gull colony returned from the seaside. They had sad little faces with tiny black spectacles, and took bread from your hand. Round and round we walked, sometimes never speaking, and I used to imagine I could hear Sandiman's brain turning over an insoluble problem. Now and then he took out a cheque book and wrote a cheque on a tree and gave it to me.

Eventually I got a job abroad and I forgot all about the Gardens. But a year later I was back, broke, and found myself back at the pond. I was not surprised to see Sandiman wearily feeding a gull, and he was not surprised to see me either. He made no reference to my having been abroad, and it seemed tactless to bring up the subject of Switzerland. However, I had to look for work and started to do a series of free-lance articles for an illustrated magazine. It was inclined to be nervous work because the editors were always getting expelled, and people didn't know who I was, and if I was rude to some-body I would go to the office and that person would suddenly have become the editor. I tried to get subjects abroad, but they were jealously appropriated by the few members of the staff who had not been shot at during the editorial revolutions. One day a completely new bullet-proof editor called me into his office. "Listen," he said, "have you ever been to the pond in Kensington Gardens? Have a go at it, and see what you can do. I will find you a good photographer."

It was high summer when the photographer and I entered the Gardens and started to walk round the pond. Kites were flying, model boats hooted, the band played, and the leaves shimmered. As usual, Sandiman was there looking down at the singed grass and wrestling inwardly. "It's a pity you're doing this," he said, after some thought. "It'll cheapen the place. I would have given you a cheque."

The photographer and I began to climb up on the band-stand, while a uniformed man with a huge moustache was conducting "Pale Hands I Loved."

"Go away," he shouted.

"We are press," I said.

At once his granite face split into an oddly surprising smile and he tore wildly at the air with his baton. We got some good pictures of tamed trombones and then hunted for kites and model boats. "And lovers," said the photographer, taking out his telescopic lens. We were tiptoeing under some trees when we suddenly heard an enormous rustling and something jumped on my back. It was a monkey.

"Albert won't hurt you," said a hearty voice. "He's that gentle but he loves jungly pranks."

A big man with a red face and a cap appeared, carrying a chain in his hand. The monkey jumped off my back, did a somersault and disappeared into another tree.

"We'll take a picture of this," said the photographer.

The red-faced man gave some endearing whistles and the monkey reappeared, as bright as a prize schoolboy. At that moment a huge policeman appeared.

"Now listen," he said. "Apes and the like are not allowed in the Gardens."

"Albert is not an ape," said the red-faced man.

"Ape or no," said the policeman, "you must remove it from the Gardens in an orderly manner before it becomes a nuisance to the public."

"This is a godsend," said the photographer, taking a swift picture of Albert and the pointing policeman. At that the policeman took a great slap at his camera and stood in front of it like the Houses of Parliament.

"It is illegal," he said, "to take pictures of apes in Kensington Gardens."

"We are press and it is not an ape," said the photographer, taking another snap.

"I don't care who you are," said the policeman. "It is an illegal animal and a misdemeanour is being committed."

We watched him escort the red-faced man and Albert, who could only proceed by trees, to the Bayswater Road.

Some time later, at a party, I met a B.B.C. producer.

"I saw your story about the pond in Kensington Gardens," he said. "Would you like to do a little story about it for the Home Chat hour?"

"Certainly," I said.

"Make it chatty," he said. "About eight minutes, and aim at the women washing up."

"Certainly," I said.

I went home, and I wrote about the monkey and the bandstand and the kites and the shimmering leaves and sent it in. Then I got a letter of acceptance and was told to report at the Home Chat room in a week.

I reported there, and found an office of about fourteen terribly conscientious women. They seemed to exude ideals, efficiency and a sort of enormous meaning. A very timid man occasionally appeared and smiled at me bashfully, and I noticed that he always moved about sideways like a crab in a dangerous aquarium. He was the Home Chat producer. I hung about in one of the rooms looking at my script and avoiding the eyes of the women, and particularly of the female director, who switched dials and pushed in knobs and ran the world and had a tiny sneer whenever she noticed me. There was also a rather large woman with a great black hat who was called Mrs. Featherstone, and who ran the Home Chat diary. I heard it over the inter-com. It was about blackberry bushes at dawn, and God, and recipes, and not wasting time. When it was my turn for rehearsal I went into a room behind a glass panel and through it I could see the female director switching dials and Mrs. Featherstone nodding her huge animistic hat. I read my script in a quavering sick tenor and waited for the result. Suddenly I heard Mrs. Featherstone's rich voice saying, very clearly, "Well, I don't think *that's* very funny, I must say." The inter-com, which should have been shut off, had been left on. I went out from the broadcasting room and the female director announced sandwiches and coffee in the board room before the genuine broadcast. We went up two flights of stairs and arrived in a large room with a big table topped by a vase of flowers.

"What beautiful flowers!" cried Mrs. Featherstone. "How they make one *think*."

"Now then," said the director, "will everyone have coffee?"

"May I have some beer?" I asked with a certain bravado. There was a long silence and then a rustling noise like the wings of insects at the end of a hot summer day.

"You may," said the director, fingering her jet necklace,

"but I warn you that it slurs the speech. Home Chat is a gossipy, family programme that rather keeps away from excess, if you understand what I mean." She rang for the waiter.

Ten minutes before the broadcast the male producer scuttled towards me. "How is it going?" he asked stealthily.

"I have been insulted," I said, "and I am not going on with it."

"Insulted," he said with horror, "on Home Chat?"

"Certainly. A woman called Mrs. Featherstone informed everybody that my talk wasn't funny."

"Not funny," cried the producer. "But I rolled. The monkey and the bandstand. I rolled."

"I'm not going on with it," I said.

"But you have to. I will speak to Mrs. Featherstone at once."

"Don't," I said.

"You're joking," cried the producer suddenly.

"Possibly," I said.

Half-way through the broadcast I suddenly thought of Sandiman listening-in in the lounge of his terrible hotel and could hardly speak. It was like trying to climb a mountain in slippery boots.

"Thank you," said the lady interviewer, and they put on a record of "Pale Hands I Loved," while I stumbled out of the room.

A few weeks later I returned to the pond. Sandiman was there and we walked three times round it without speaking.

"I read the article," he said eventually, "and I heard the broadcast. And what have you gained from it?"

"Not much, I suppose," I said.

The leaves were falling, and the gulls had returned, eyeing us skimpily through their little black spectacles, and the kites raced in the wind. Sandiman went to a tree and wrote me a cheque.

68

About a month later the pond froze and it was covered with mist. Shrouded cries of birds penetrated the fog, and I had a sudden feeling we were walking round the North Pole. I could hardly see Sandiman walking beside me.

"I have come to a decision," I said. "I am going to write about the broadcast."

I turned to Sandiman but he had gone and all I could hear was the mournful hoot of a polar bird.

TROUBLED BY SEAGULLS

A<small>T LAST</small> I had to get a job in an Income Tax office. All winter there was a gust of coughing and a rustling of forms. In the centre of my department was a kind of glass box in which sat Mr. Beamish. When I first met him I thought him a jolly sort of man, the sort of man who would make the ideal uncle, conjuring tricks, cricket bats and dressing up as Father Christmas. He cracked one or two Inland Revenue jokes and showed me to my desk. After that he never smiled at me again. He hated writers, except those who signed cheques. He only unbent when certain favoured officials congregated in his box, and then they all roared with laughter over index cards, and stared outwards into the room. Beamish himself seemed to have photo-electric eyes and I could feel them singeing the back of my neck while I sat at my desk, watching seagulls. Sometimes he would call me into the box and at other times he would come out of the box and look over my shoulder. Frequently, when he did this, I would be writing a poem on the back of a Schedule D form. A poem which never went right. Mr. Beamish was not concerned about the technical problems which beset writers, he just sat or stood there loathing me. Perhaps his main reason for loathing me was that I could not be sacked. There I was, and unless I did something overt, like breaking windows or introducing snakes, I could be there for ever.

Beamish's second-in-command was a man called Thrush. He was balding, with a sharp chin, and wore armbands. It took some time for me to discover his place in the Inland Revenue Secret Police. He padded about the room with apparent inoffensiveness, making remarks about the weather and even telling jokes. Everybody warned me against him immediately. Every ten minutes he would slip into the glass box and, under the pretence of laughing over an index card, would pass on his information. The next in superiority was a very jolly woman called Dot. In her spare time she organised ping-pong competitions (and when she played Beamish she always won. Beamish had a kind of Boer War gallantry towards her or any other woman in the department), and she often screamed with laughter in the silent, bloodless room or cried "Stop it, you," to a bold clerk when they met over an index box. Beamish paid no attention, although he would have reacted to a fly walking over an assessment form in triplicate at the far end of the room. I soon found myself on jolly terms with Dot, but in no time at all everyone warned me against her, and I must say that I was very surprised when Thrush padded over to me one day and hinted that she was not to be trusted.

One day I muddled the names on a form and the papers were passed on and dealt with, the original mistake multiplying itself like a snowball. Unfortunately the names involved belonged to two rival greengrocers, and the case took a lot of thrashing out, besides turning nasty. Both the greengrocers rushed into the glass box and made a scene. I felt very sorry for Beamish, who despised tax-payers as a race beneath him, but was glad to see him control the situation with icy contempt, so that the greengrocers crept out of the box, presum-

71

ably quite penniless. The next day Thrush bent over my desk. "Mr. Beamish wishes to see you," he said in a soft, papery voice. He looked like a cardboard hangman. Poisoned ink, paper-clip stilettos and suffocation by forms. I went into the glass box and shut the door. Outside the glass everyone was watching me and Beamish, scanning the least movement. Avid for the first hint of something, a fist, tears, a slammed door. Few, except the permanent officials, could afford the films and they were too tired to read novels. I faced Beamish, trying to look like something he would recognise. Trying not to look like a gypsy, a refugee from the Promenade des Anglais, a lost dog or a seagull. But it was no good.

"Carson," he said, "I tried to give you a chance. Didn't I?"

"Mr. Beamish, I . . ."

"Answer me," he said. "Did I try to give you a chance?"

"Certainly," I answered. "You gave me the L.C.C. male employees."

"Are you trying to be funny?" he asked coldly. "Because if you are I would like to point this out to you. This department cannot tolerate slackness. The Nation is working at full speed, not playing the fool. I have been watching you. Are you aware of that? You write doggerel and you have been interfering with Mrs. Stoat." (This was Dot.) I didn't say anything. Any more than I did to C.O.s in the army. But I watched Beamish's avuncular face and couldn't help thinking that he wasn't acting true to type. He should have offered me a cigar and said he understood. With a chuckle and a piece of mellow advice about keeping up appearances. But he didn't. "You'll have to go to Room A," he said.

This was terrible. Inland Revenue couldn't sack you but it could send you down to a dungeon full of prehistoric index-cards, Carblott, Carraway, Carsle, Carter, Carver. Down there it was dark, lonely and damp with the forlorn enterprises of Dipper, Dipserman, Dipsey, Diptick, and Dipyard. There were avenues of alphabetical hopelessness, deathly quiet, except for the occasional shrill laughter of a small mad clerk who was permanently in charge of the room. His name was Dipple. I spent a month there, starting at Conger, Coniton, and getting as far as Copley, when I was released and sent back upstairs.

I had lunch at the Civil Service canteen. After lunch one could go out on a sort of parapet and look over the rumbling town. London. I could watch the seagulls in the smoky sky and think, "They aren't called Hamperton, Hampsley, Hampton, Hargreaves, Hatcham, or Haw." They hovered over Oxford Street, glided to the river and went keening to the great green sea. I took walks with a temporary called Hansom. Everywhere seemed suspicious, premeditated, furtive and terrifying. Inland Revenue had poisoned my sap. It must be happening everywhere. This way, Modom, gleaming flowers, shall I wrap it up, and behind, in the shadows, taxis and neat rats in armbands. Everybody taxing everybody else, nobody believing in anything, Carblott eating Carghill, Carghill eating Carraway and Carter reading about it in his newspaper in the tube. I often wanted to shout out in the street.

I walked along beside Hansom. Inwardly I was waving to myself. Far away the peacocks were crying, the bells were ringing, the ships were sailing the China Seas. I strained my ears to hear the fairy music, but it was drowned in the roar of traffic, and the dreamless austerity faces of the shoppers, like aggressive utensils, broke any vestige of a spell. Yes, a spell, that was what I was waiting for. Not the taxable commodity. Not the rodent cunning of supply and demand. But there was no magic anywhere apart from the swirl of the seagulls in the sky. I heard Hansom saying, "The correct kind of tie should have some sort of colour, but only in a subdued way. And it should match the socks." He bought an evening paper and looked at the theatre news. He talked about Jesse,

73

Noel, Larry and Donald. He never said a word against any of them, not at their cruellest hour. For that matter, he never said a word against anybody, and never talked office gossip. Dot, Thrush, Beamish, and Drake and all of them were sweet. He even volunteered for the dungeons. I used to take over the newspaper when he had finished and turn to the book reviews. I used to imagine myself reading "Mr. Carson's unforgettable character studies of Wackstead, Wadley, Wadlington and Wagstaff . . ."

Summer came and then, far away somewhere, the golden rod held court in the burnished fields and the tawny sun drank the cold dew. The apples fell and the swallows crossed off the days. I began to make a friend of a man called Frost. He was large, with a very solid appearance, and sat quietly and confidently rustling through index-cards, without Beamish's eye ever burning the back of his neck. He had a very distinguished war-record and a mass of medals from Burma, but he put all that behind him and faced the future with unromantic resolution. Frost was looking round for a suitable position in the city and he spent a few afternoons of Civil Service leave being interviewed by people in Threadneedle Street. Tin, rubber, oil. He was married and showed me a photograph of his wife, Muriel. "She tells everyone I'm a terribly important man in Inland Revenue. It's our standing joke." I liked Frost. He seemed imperturbable and he had lived with adventure.

When winter came, I made another mistake and was turned into an assistant counter man. The counter was directly in front of the glass box. At first it was refreshing to be in touch with the public. Good morning, lovely morning, index number please, you won't be kept long. Most of the people were furious directly they appeared. They quivered with rage.

"This is preposterous," they would cry, waving a form.

"It is preposterous," I would reply. "This is a preposterous place altogether."

74

I had many interesting conversations.

One afternoon I was having a conversation with an elderly gentleman about birth control, and I was conscious of a figure standing beside me. It was Thrush. He gave a sickly smile, coughed up a joke, and darted into the glass box. I saw him talking obliquely to the Inspector, and could see Beamish's eye was upon me. I was called in.

"Have you any idea why I put you to work on that counter?" he asked with an angry point.

"To help," I said.

I was frightened of Beamish as I was frightened of all elderly administrators, officials, policemen, colonels or judges. There is a perpetual net for the butterflies. They can catch you for arson, witchcraft, sodomy, soliciting, contempt, vagrancy. They can prove you mad, without means of support, unborn or dead. They can bury you in unconsecrated ground. You have to fly very hard to keep in the sun.

"Precisely," said Beamish, "to help. You were called on to obtain the index number of the client and immediately contact the tax officer required. Immediately. The work of this department is geared so as to lose no time whatever. In future you will limit yourself to saying 'good-day,' discovering the client's reference number, contacting the appropriate officer and *leaving the counter* at once until the next client appears. That is all."

It was like Russia. I had never known the Russia of life, apart from the eternal army. Simply going about shops and buying things, cashing an occasional cheque at a bank, getting a passport, signing my name in a registry office for ration books or marriage. Good-day, sir. Shall I wrap it up? How is Mrs. Carson? This Russian world of the everyday was marvellous, preposterous, infinitely alarming. How did they do it and go on doing it? I carried on at the counter, your reference number please, someone for you, Mr. Mask, hotel mani-

75

curist. Mr. Beastleworth is here, Mr. Drake, you weren't in yesterday. I started to grow thin and pale and the moths had got at my one suit. The only poetry left in my life, apart from the seagulls, was afforded by clients with improper proper names, preferably those who were hopelessly over-taxed. I shared these names with Frost. We used to walk over to the counter and gloat over them. Frost, old chap, come and look at Mr. Fallus.

But something had happened to Frost. His clothes were beginning to hang round him. I could see him staring out of the window, looking at seagulls. I know he was waving to him-self. He was on the wrong train. One day I discovered him in a corner of the department, tearing up forms.

"But, my dear chap," I said, incredibly startled.

"Don't be silly," he said, "they all do it. Even Thrush does it from time to time."

He stuffed fragments of forms in an O.H.M.S. envelope and walked over to the stove. For days I thought about the whole thing and then I decided to join him. Together we sat side by side, out of view of the box, and disposed of Dimble, Dimmer, Dippleby, Dipsey . . .

⌐⌐⌐⌐⌐⌐⌐⌐⌐⌐⌐

YOU CAN'T
BEAT MAGIC CARPETS

I WAS out of a job, when someone gave me an introduction to
the Staff Manager of a travel agency called Magic Carpets.
His name was Mr. Prout. I went around to the Magic Carpets office in Baker Street and asked for him. I was put into a
waiting-room, and found a number of people there, hanging
around like myself, talking to each other in German, French,
Italian and Spanish. I got into conversation with some of them
and discovered they were all English and expecting jobs from
Mr. Prout. Not only as couriers, but as representatives or assistant representatives at the various centres at home and
abroad. I learned that the representative and assistant representative were considered more respectable than the courier,
whose life was adventurous but tough.

"He's all right, if he can fend for himself," said a pompous-
looking man in a trilby, "but personally I wouldn't touch it.
Give me a nice little hotel in Aix, and you can keep the
trains."

Eventually Mr. Prout sent for me, and I went upstairs to
the office.

77

Mr. Prout, tall and thin and precisely dressed, was seated behind a desk. He looked at me carefully for a few moments and then asked routine questions. What were my languages? French, Italian and Spanish, I said. My French was fairly good, my Italian poor, my Spanish worse. But I didn't tell him that. I was given a short test which I passed. Where had I been educated? Marlborough College and various crammers for Oxford. I never made the grade. Went to New Zealand and pulled dung off sheep's bottoms. But I didn't tell him that. "Public-school boy, eh?" he said. I gave him an Empire-builder look. "Well, so you want to be a courier. Well, you can't fool around with women or booze on duty. Now then, to be a courier, do you know what you want? I'll tell you. You want the hide of a rhinoceros, the patience of Job and the strength of a lion. Everything's your fault. Everything. If the train's late, if the food's bad, if it rains, if somebody runs off with somebody else's wife, it's your fault. You've got to improvise. You've got to smile. You've got to get the people through. But I'll tell you the most important thing of all. A sense of humour." He gave me an intensely curious look. "You *must have a sense of humour*. Listen. Have you heard this story?" He then, with a very earnest face, told me a dirty story. So I told him another one, and he told me another. Then he made a note on his pad and said, "Sense of humour seems all right. Mind you, nothing of this to the other executives. It's just my way." He held out his hand. "I'll let you know in a few days if you're engaged."

Two days later I received a letter from Magic Carpets, offering me the job as courier at six pounds a week.

When I presented myself to Mr. Prout he told me to see Grasp, the chief courier. "Don't worry if he's unpleasant," he said, "it's liver trouble." I went to his office, which was on the same floor. A notice on the door said, "GRASP, Chief Courier. Knock. This means YOU." I knocked.

"Come in," growled a voice, and I went in. "So you're Carson," said the voice, the owner flinging down a time-table. "Yes," I said.

He had a long nose, red hair and angry eyes. "So," he said, rubbing his hands. "So. This is the sort of thing they are sending me now as couriers."

"It is," I said, going red in the face, but holding myself back. Over Grasp's flaming head was a notice. TRY. WHEN THINGS GO WRONG TRY AGAIN.

"Report back here in May. I don't want to see you till then."

"But what do I do till May?"

"I don't know," shouted Grasp. "Ask Prout."

Prout took me to see the manager, Mr. Parkinson. "You can help with the programmes till Grasp wants you," said Parkinson. "It's quite easy, and you'll be with the other chaps." So I went downstairs to a kind of basement where they kept the Accounts Department. There was a large table in the centre of the room around which were seated a number of depressed-looking men stuffing pamphlets into envelopes. I joined them. Next to me sat the superior man who had been wearing the trilby and who wanted a nice little hotel in Aix.

"This is terribly infra-dig," he said, reaching for a pamphlet. "They should get boys."

I opened one of the pamphlets, which was entitled "LET MAGIC CARPETS WAFT YOU AWAY." On the cover was a picture of a man and a woman, the type of people who do everything in advertisements and whom everybody loathes, sitting on a carpet, and looking down on mountains. Inside was a selection of weekly and fortnightly holidays to be arranged in hotels, chalets, *palazzi*, and community centres in Europe. "Let Magic Carpets give you the holiday you have dreamed of . . . Romantic Austria . . . Mysterious Spain . . . Unforgettable Paris . . . Hob-nob with gay continentals on the

79

sparkling Riviera . . . relax in an intimate hotel with every comfort and services included . . . or expand in a house-party atmosphere at one of our chalets overlooking a sparkling Swiss lake." Then there were suggestions and prices. Seven days at Tremezzo, the Hotel Romantico. Seven days in Montreux, the Magic Carpets' chalet. Forty-five pounds. Or a fortnight in San Remo at the Hotel Amoroso. Or there were cruises. See ancient Greece, the Parthenon, etc., by comfortable motor-coach, visiting Paris (stopping at Notre-Dame, Eiffel Tower, Folies Bergère, etc.). We were given lists of names of those who had answered advertisements in the Press and wrote them on the envelopes. Mrs. Smith, The Laurels, Ealing. Mr. Brown, The Elms, Cleethorpes.

The days went by in this mechanical routine. Mr. Sharpe, Mrs. Shipley, Miss Shore, Mr. Sidman, Miss Simms. As we worked in a basement, I couldn't look out of the window and watch any seagulls. There was a tension between the accounts clerks and the pamphlet-pushers. Temporarily we were doing menial work, and at the same time we appeared more grand and less respectable than the clerks. They, after all, audited the world we travelled in. They coughed when the windows were opened and laughed over bookings. In a corner of the room was a glass box where the accounts manager sat, keeping his eye on activities in the department. I could feel his eyes burning the back of my neck. The adding machines ticked, typewriters tapped, the seagull had betrayed me. Mrs. Marks, Mr. Masters, Miss Matt, Mrs. Maw, Mr. Maxton.

All my companions felt more or less the same, in varying degrees. Some were new like myself, others had been with the firm for years. There had always been this ritual, like the sacrifice to the sun-god. In May they went out to their glory, their *plages*, their palm-studded *palazzi*, and their American bars, and in the winter they were divested and mocked, and became the butt of the clerks, doing any sort of odd job which didn't require specialised knowledge. Even among themselves there were subtle rivalries. Although they all sat together at the same table sending pamphlets to Miss Tawnish, Mr. Teal, Miss Tench and Mrs. Tester, they were privately separated by social distinctions and taboos. Representatives, or "reps" as they were called, jostled with assistant reps and couriers and flinched inwardly. And even the classes were sub-divided. Certain Magic Carpets holiday centres were superior, for various reasons, to others, and a rep who came from Lucerne felt above one at Interlaken. Thus an assistant at Antwerp roughly equalled a rep at Lucerne or two reps at Interlaken. The lowest representative was the station rep who looked after Magic Carpets clients as they passed through the main continental junctions. He stood slightly lower than the American Tours courier, the aristocrat of the conductors. The rest of the couriers worked down from the Italian Cruise conductor to the Lucerne-run courier. Custer had shared this with another man called Ball.

Certain of the continental men never turned up at the pamphlet table at all. They retired for the winter, or had sinecure jobs in other parts of the office, or lectured in the Midlands on Magic Carpets in Switzerland. The Paris rep, for instance, was hardly ever visible. I saw him once, coming out of a lavatory, wearing a Homburg and gloves and a distinguished stoop. (Even his assistant rep was reserved, read Proust, and lost no dignity from sending a programme to Miss Brown, Chez Moi, Acton.) And the American Tours courier, who wore an astrakhan coat and a small imperial beard, only turned up to collect his pay. "Got to get back to my contacts," he said once.

I wasn't in the pamphlet dungeon all the time. To add further gall to the cup of the winter-time continentals, all of us were called on to do odd jobs as sweepers, package-removers, coal-heavers and messenger-boys. The clerks enjoyed every minute of it, tapping their machines with manicured nails and sneering over their carbons. Only the assistant Paris rep refused to co-operate, rising, picking up his cane, quoting something nasty from Gide, and leaving. I was glad of any inter-.ruption from Miss Naseby, Mr. Nat, Miss Neave, and Mrs. Nest, and made the most of visiting the other departments in the building.

The Magic Carpets building contained an enormous organisation aimed at luring the holiday-maker, snaring him, packing him off on excursions, and pouring him back to London. Everything was done for him. He needn't speak a word of a foreign language, or worry about tickets, passport visas or room accommodation. At every station he was met by a Magic Carpets uniformed man, handed over to a courier, and met at his destination by an assistant rep, who also nursed him at his hotel. All this entailed enormous activity, and numerous departments. On the basement floor was Accounts and Correspondence Sales. The latter was an enormous room full of desks and dictaphones where clerks dealt with correspondence and costing of individual Magic Carpets holidays. There were two sections, British and Foreign. Voices shouted names of foreign towns into their machines, Berne, Montreux, Brussels, Rome, Naples, Madrid. "Dear Miss Jones, as per form, we can supply you with a room with bath at the Hotel Excitico, Cadenabbia, for seven days. The V form also includes excursions to Milan, Lake Lugano and the Rhône Glacier." (V forms are issued by banks to agencies to cover hotel-excursion payments abroad. They are deducted from the travel allowance. The remainder is spending money. Payment of transportation to any destination abroad does not affect the travel allowance.) On the ground floor was the Sales Office for the general public, decorated with Magic Carpets posters, the office of the director, and the Publicity Department. This department also included a film section. This was one smallish man who sat in motor-coaches taking pictures through the window. On the second floor was the Rates Department, which kept current particulars and prices of first- and second-class hotels at home and abroad. Single rooms, double rooms, balcony rooms, balcony rooms with bath, in season and out of season. Plus *taxe de séjour*, police tax, service. Minus a percentage for the agency. Prices were converted into English currency and lists sent over to Sales. Everyone in the building was always ringing up Rates. "Some chap here wants to go to Jericho. Got a cheap, clean hotel?" They were always bad-tempered and slammed doors. On the third floor were the typists and duplicating machines presided over by a frightening woman called Miss Trigger. She was a sort of female Grasp. They hated each other. You could make a firm friend of Grasp by insulting her. On the same floor was the Manager's Office and Grasp's office.

I carried on in the basement until the pamphlets gave out. By now spring had definitely opened the door to summer, and the air in the streets was light as banter. The English, coshed, influenza-ridden and stoically guilty, began to creep out of their shells. The Censor had been forced to let Flora through. There were bunches of pretty girls about, and you could actually hear laughter in Leicester Square. Wars, atom bombs, peace conferences, murders and the lethal platitudes of politicians did not seem to matter so much. The earth, for a short moment, had come into its own. It glowed like a woman in love. And at last Grasp sent for me.

"Ah," said Grasp, "you're late." He pounded his fist on the table. "There's one thing I won't tolerate in this place, and that's lateness. Not even a minute. This job deals with exactly timed arrivals and departures and punctuality is essential. If you can't be on time, you'd better do something else." He cocked his head on one side and looked at me. "You look bet-

83

ter, at any rate. That's a nice suit. How much did you pay for it?"

"Three guineas," I said. "It's second hand."

Grasp gave a surprising snort of laughter. "Well, you can start travelling," he said.

"When?" I asked.

"Tomorrow. Fleet of charabancs going all round London. The sights. Tower of London. Buckingham Palace. End up at the Houses of Parliament. A crowd of sightseers from Lancashire. They'll be received by their M.P."

"What do I do?" I asked.

"Tell them about London," said Grasp.

I daren't tell him I knew nothing about London. I'd lived there for years but I didn't know one monument from another. I only knew Piccadilly Circus, the Load of Hay and Selfridge's.

"All right," I said. "When do I start?"

"Ten o'clock tomorrow. Get your hair cut."

I stood outside the Magic Carpets office the next morning until the charabancs turned up. A Magic Carpets official pointed to one of the coaches and I got in. It drove off. As it drove down Oxford Street to Piccadilly Circus, I was invaded by panic. What are these buildings? Desperately I read the names of the streets. After a few minutes I was met by hearty, tolerant laughter. We reached Lambeth Bridge. The coach broke down. I looked at the square, expectant faces of my passengers, and remembered what Prout had said about a sense of humour. "This is the Thames," I said. Two minutes later I said, "This is the Thames." I kept on repeating this, until I suddenly knew the sight-seers were on my side. A kind lady from Maccleston offered to take over the tour. She had been in London before, for a day visit, and remembered the important buildings. I sat back in my seat while she cried out, "Shell Mex House, Horse Guards Parade, Admiralty Arch!"

⌐⌐⌐⌐⌐⌐⌐⌐⌐⌐

SWISS MANOEUVRES

AT LAST Magic Carpets sent me abroad to collect passengers travelling on collective party tickets and bring them back to Victoria. My first assignment was in Switzerland. Montreux. I was to stay the night there and bring a party back the next day. When I arrived in Montreux it was raining. I was received by the chief Magic Carpets representative and given a hotel and dinner. I met the assistant reps, who took me to a café near the station. It had weary palms, and was full of Magic Carpets clients. A band played "Annie Laurie" and "Mighty Like a Rose." The assistant reps rushed about the café, being arch to plain girls, making boisterous jokes about Swiss rolls, and then quickly subsided into boredom and melancholy. "For God's sake talk to me about London," said one of them to me. "This place is incredibly false. Switzerland has the depth of a post-card."

In Montreux I learnt how to fight the war of compart-ment labels. The Montreux–Paris train comes from Italy, ripe with confusion. The Magic Carpets representative has ordered a carriage from Milan. The Milan uniformed man (his name was Emilio Pestaloggi) has plastered the carriage with Magic Carpets labels. He has bribed the guard to lock the door. Just before the train leaves another agency bribes the guard to unlock the door, strip off the Magic Carpets labels, and substitute their own. The Italian public, of all publics, cannot stand to see empty compartments plastered with notices. They pile into the train like woodlice into a rotten tree trunk, portmanteaux, children, birdcages and sausages. They fall on the guard and beat him up. He unlocks the door.

After a few months of this the Montreux rep cabled Domodossola MEET TRAIN WITH LABELS. The whole operation started again. Some of the compartments got through. But by now Magic Carpets considered Montreux a strategic point and built up a plan of campaign. I arrived there for its inception. The party of tourists, who can only move as a group on party-reduction tickets (the one master ticket is held by the courier; he travels free), stood half-way up the station platform, strong men to the front, vigorous women next, weak women, invalids and children at the back. I stood to the left, armed with labels. Dotted about the platform were twelve Lucerne assistant reps. In the centre stood the chief representative, carrying a stout stick (his name was Benshaw). A Swiss uniformed man was stationed up on the roof, his eyes glued to binoculars, a whistle in his mouth. One blast meant labelled carriages to the rear, and three meant no labelled carriages. Four blasts meant there was only one engine.

On the blast of the whistle we performed the manœuvre we had carefully rehearsed. I waved desperately to my group and ran towards the rear or the front of the train. People immediately began to pour out (Montreux is a popular resort, God knows why) and the assistant reps parked them to one side, while the strong party-ticket men boarded the train. Other assistant reps entered at the other end, converging on the Magic Carpets compartments and winkling out any interlopers (if the door had been unlocked). Then suitcases, women and children were pushed through the open windows into possible safety. There were various troubles with this method. The train always started again very quickly, and as many as five assistant reps had been carried on to Lausanne. Or the Swiss uniformed men had made a mistake and the reserved coaches were at the other end. This led to a free fight after the train had moved off, and I would wave frantically out of the window to the diminishing face of Benshaw.

If there were no labelled carriages at all, we all converged on the least empty compartments, bribed the guard (or tried to—this also led to incidents) and turned everybody out, while I plastered up labels. The people left with amazing dexterity, mothers with nursing children, old ladies, cripples, wounded soldiers. I think they were numbed and dismayed by large quantities of English. After the Magic Carpets clients had been settled (smashing holiday at Shilly-Chalet, pity we have to have this. No organisation) I spent the rest of the time with the people I had turned out. (*"Vous n'avez pas l'air d'un Anglais, monsieur. Pas du tout."*)

It is easy to dismiss Switzerland. It is over-spotless and prophylactic. The mountains look as though millions of charwomen got up at dawn to scrub them down with soap and water. The towns give you ready-reckoning smiles, how much are you worth now, how much will you be worth next summer. Everywhere is a ticking of precision watches, a filling of platinum fountain pens, a packing of cheeses, a netting of nylons. There has been no war. The air is fat with peace. The solid townsmen sit back in their gleaming cafés and read enormous dull newspapers. They eat huge badly cooked meals. Civilisation is here, boring, luminous, pedantic. Four countries live together, parochially disliking each other, but still living together. It is a country of exactitude, of perfect prose, where poets die.

From Montreux I climbed by funicular to the Rochers de Naye, up to a world of wild carnations and geraniums, neat

87

as jewels, where the marmots whistle to each other among the crags. I called on a farmer and a woman gave me a bowl of milk. Children came and sat on the grass beside me, friendship and peace and laughter grew so quickly. I felt I had been there all my life.

"Do you always live here?" I asked the woman.

"Oh, no," she answered. "When it gets too hot, we move down in the valley over there." She pointed over towards the crags. There was a dip of about two thousand feet.

"And when do you go down to the lake?" I asked, pointing towards the silver tray of Lake Leman beneath us.

"Oh, we've never been down *there*," she said. "They say it's unhealthy and the people are so queer."

During my spells abroad in Switzerland, I became a Magic Carpets pilgrim. Couriers stay at agency hotels free of charge. I wandered from place to place, calling on hotel representatives for board and lodging, covered with mud and drinking on luxury loggias while the orchestra played "Tea for Two" for Miss Smith, Mr. Robinson, Miss Brown and Mrs. Jones. Or I toured the lakes in a dazzling white steamer, drinking kirsch in the dining saloon and calling in at little towns twinkling as snug and sweet as a cherry in a martini cocktail. Or joining in Magic Carpets excursions to monasteries and castles. Or eating my way through the *plats du jour* of three hundred and ninety regions of La Suisse Romande, Schweizer-Deutsch, Ricinese, and Craubunden in the vast, cathedral-like buffet of the Lausanne railway buffet.

One day I was climbing up a crag near Les Avants when I saw a familiar figure outlined against the sky. It turned its head, and I recognised the severe features of Mr. Thrush. On his annual holiday. I approached him quietly from behind. Should I push?

Should I? No one would know. He was dressed in precisely the same clothes as he wore in the office. Even the armbands were there, to protect him against rocks, brambles, lizards, and the unknown. Just a gentle push. But it was an idle fancy. No one pushes the Mr. Thrushes of this world off crags. They don't even fall off. They don't even jump off. Leave that to the beautiful and the brave. I touched his shoulder and he gave a start. "Why," he said, "fancy meeting you." He adjusted his hat. "It's a small world. I'm staying at Montreux. I do every year. With the wife and kids. Edward, Enid, Estelle and Esther. How high, by the way, is that mountain? They give it at 5,333 feet. But an expert I met in the train said it was 4,999 feet. I am going to borrow a theodolite."

As we climbed down, he told me a joke. It was about an incident in Swiss Inland Revenue, and had occurred in 1925. It concerned four people called Geissman, Gelder, Goldschmidt and Gorblatter.

A POEM OF TRAINS

As TIME went on I learnt the philosophy of trains. The French trains belch foul smoke, and in the morning you wake under a shell of ashes. But they stop. In the silence you hear the earth breathing and ghosts crying the names of the towns. Through the steamy night the goats bleat, the engines pant, there is the rush of feet on gravel, the thud of luggage, long goodbyes. Patient people are saying goodbye, aunts go back to lonely homes. Children to new cities. Voices come down the corridors, families, friends and lovers making themselves into safe, joking islands. For these trains at night are phantoms; they are ferrying the dead. In the morning there is the resurrection. The lavabo calls. Long queues with towels and self-control. I didn't sleep a wink, my dear. Somebody in our carriage was eating garlic. *Bonjour chérie, bien dormi?* Then we are at Vallorbe. The air is crisp as new bread. In the buffet are bowls of gallant coffee, croissants, cherry jam and jugs of steaming milk. In the distance there is a lapping, a chattering of mountain water.

The train officials are trim, you treat them with punctilio. Then the engine changes and you can lean out of the carriage window breathing the sweet electric air. Past the great lake

90

of Leman, blue as a child's dream of heaven, past the toy-
like clang of the station bells, and on through the long anti-
septic rush inside the Simplon tunnel, into the operatic arms
of the Italian customs.

I love the English trains from Victoria, elbowing their way
primly through tunnels, and disgorging endless cups of tea
and biscuits. Nothing emotional, no drama. At Dieppe all is
changed. The trains are prima donnas. They stamp their feet,
their whistles shriek "I am going this very instant," and, like
women, they stay and stay till love goes cold. Then, when you
take no notice, they've suddenly left. And the rails and the
farmhouses are knocked away, the train only wants Paris, Paris
and the Place Pigalle.

⎾⎿⎾⎿⎾⎿⎾⎿⎾⎿⎾⎿⎿

THE LAKE OF LIES

ONE DAY Grasp called me into the office and told me to sit down. "You're promoted," he said. "You're going to be an assistant rep. That means you're out of my hands . . . worse luck." He grinnéd. "After all, I've been a good influence. Made you punctual, cut your hair and all that. Don't like that tie, though. You're too arty, that's the trouble with you. Go and see the manager."

I went to another office and saw Mr. Frunley, the manager.

"Well, Carson," he said, "I see you have had a good education, and you have a sound report. I've decided to have you sent to Castagnuola, in Switzerland. You'll work under a man called Box. Remarkable man. Keep the Magic Carpets flag flying. You will travel by free pass to Lucerne, stay the night at Shilly-Chalet and go on to Castagnuola."

When I told the people in the office I was going to be Box's assistant in Lugano, they roared with laughter.

"Why?" I asked.

"You'll see," they said.

I heard various rumours about him. He ran a vice ring. Two assistant reps had mysteriously disappeared. He was a blackmailer who knew too much about Magic Carpets, and couldn't be removed. I asked Custer about him.

"Oh, old Box," he said, with a smile. "He's an odd chap. He's been in Castagnuola for years. I once took a party out there, and when I returned to the station, the police were waiting for me. They told me I was a Rumanian spy. Wanted for bigamy. That was Box. He imitates people very well. Nobody really knows who he is. You might get on with him all right. And you should find any amount of rackets in Castagnuola. Smuggling and so on. It's on the Italian border."

I set out with my passes and reached Basel, where I bought myself a suit and had lunch with the station representative, a man called Sand. "Quite a job, all this," he said, waving his arm about to include the railway lines, the trains, the porters, the kiosks and the smoke. He was a short, fat man with a moustache, and gave the impression that he owned the whole station. In fact he hardly ever moved from it. He ate in the buffet, sat in his private office with a telephone and a time-table, and awaited the arrival of Miss Robinson, Mr. Robson, Mrs. Rochaway and Mr. Rockthorpe. He exuded a sort of power which he must have absorbed from the railway engines and the crowds. Anywhere else he would have been completely inconspicuous, a type of minor civil servant. Here he bustled about and got in the way of the stationmaster, the assistant stationmaster, the telegraphists, and the customs officers. All over a Mr. Pitman or a Miss Pitter. He rushed me into the buffet and took charge of the waitresses. "Order what you like," he said, as though he was going to pay for it himself. I had noticed this habit with most Magic Carpets representatives, who gave themselves an air of distributing largesse, when in fact all such bills were paid by the hotels, stations or restaurants. "It's a good life," said Sand over lunch. "They consider me someone of importance. I feed well, meet people. Girls."

He winked at me. "All here, in the station. Do you see that waitress over there? Near the cash desk? Her name's Lulu. Thinks the world of me." After lunch he took me to my train, showing me how the thing was done, supervising the Magic Carpets uniformed man, arguing with the porters, and finally waving me goodbye with an air of triumph.

When I arrived at Lucerne, I took a taxi to Shilly-Chalet. It was an enormous Swiss-style building overlooking the lake. I walked up the drive, into the courtyard and pushed open the iron-studded door. The hall was spacious and hung with antlers and hunting-horns. There was a large sham-antique table covered with copies of *Punch, Picture Post, Ideal Home* and various digests. On the walls were typewritten notices. "Tea is served punctually at four-thirty. Hot buttered scones, crumpets and toast are available if required." "Bridge social tonight at eight-thirty." "There is a service of Morning Prayers every morning at seven-thirty. On Sundays there is a ten o'clock service in the Magic Carpets chapel. All are welcome." I looked around the hall in a state of despair, as though I was destined to carry around an Income Tax office with me wherever I went. Past the hall, in the lounge, I could hear the clicking of knitting needles, and someone had got "Take It from Here" on the wireless. Then I saw a man called Hipman, whom I had once met in the London office and who turned out to be the Lucerne representative. Since he had just been demoted from Antwerp, he was looking very moody and superior, and coldly handed me over to the housekeeper, Mrs. Chart. "I pity you going to Castagnuola," he said with a sneer. "Box is no gentleman."

The gong rang and I went in to dinner. The Magic Carpets padre said grace, and we started eating. I found myself sitting next to a rather pretty girl, who told me her name was Gladys. After dinner I took up her to my room and we sat on the bed

94

looking out of the small window at the lake. It was as beautiful and expressionless as a film-star. "It's like a dream," said Gladys, "but it's not what I expected. I'd saved up for it so long." She looked very pathetic. After some persuasion she started to undress, quite quickly, because she was abroad.

"What did you expect?" I asked her.

"Something more romantic. Peasants and strange sorts of music. Like being a gypsy. It's all excursions and ping-pong. And the people are so old. It's easy to miss things, isn't it?" Then she dressed again. There was a knock at the door.

"Oh," said Gladys in a loud agonised whisper.

"Who is it?" I cried.

"It's Mrs. Chart," said a voice. I could hear a jangle of keys, as though she were a jailer. "I came to see if you were all right," she said. Then her feet tapped away down the corridor.

"Snooping," said Gladys.

"I suppose I'll get the sack," I said.

She made up her mouth clumsily, and then turned to me, looking at me with a sort of enquiry and wonder. "I must get back to my fiancé," she said, picking up her bag.

Later that evening, there was a film show in the lounge. "From Mine to Fireplace. A History of Coal." Followed by a Mickey Mouse. Hipman called me aside. "Listen, Carson," he said. "You've been fooling about with a girl. Mrs. Chart tracked you. We have no time for that, you know. Magic Carpets doesn't run brothels. If this had been Antwerp I'd have sent you back to the London office. Of course Castagnuola may suit you very well. Box has no standards."

In the morning I set off for Castagnuola. The station bells rang and gradually the colour of the mountains, valleys and trees became richer, a whisper of Italy was in the air. Then I had arrived, and I stood by the Lake of Lugano. I fell in love with it at once. It was an intimate flirt of a lake. I could see that at once. Nothing of your Grand Como or imposing Maggiore. No place for operatic stars, famous authors, asthmatic statesmen.

Box's headquarters were in the Hotel Cosmos, so I set off to see him. Directly I asked for him at the reception desk the clerk burst out laughing. "First door on the left," he said. I went to the door, which was half open, and saw three people, an enormous woman in mauve, a plump man with a Swiss face seated at a desk, and a shortish man with a yellowish skin who appeared to be wearing a wig. There was something oddly distinguished about him.

"Yes, madam," said this man. "Tea is served in the lounge, but if you require lemon, you have to get your own."

"My own?" said the mauve lady in an astonished voice.

"Yes. There is a little fruit shop up on the left."

The lady left the office muttering, "Get my own lemons, what next. I am going to write to Magic Carpets at once."

I entered the office and introduced myself. The man whom I took to be Box took no notice, but picked up a telephone and began talking in rapid dialect.Then he replaced the receiver. "Our representative in Zurich has been shot," he said quietly. The Swiss looked quite impassive. Then Box turned to me. "So you are Carson. The police have called about you. You passed through Lucerne, I believe?"

"Yes," I replied, "I did."

"They are returning. However, it is nothing to do with me. You will take over the Hotel Paradiso, further up the lake. Can you blow a trumpet?"

"No," I said, alarmed.

"Then you will have to learn. All representatives here belong to the band. We rehearse each Saturday in the boathouse."

I left the office and sat in the Cosmos lounge. Out of curiosity, I called to one of the waiters. "Can I have tea with lemon?" I asked.

"Certainly, sir, why not?"

"I understood one had to bring one's own," I said.

The waiter looked for some time at me, and then his face broke into a smile. "*Ecco*," he said, "that is a *Boxismo*. That is what we call the sayings of Signor Box." He hurried back to the kitchen and I could hear an explosion of laughter, and cries of "*Che bello!* They must bring their own lemon." I got my tea and was presently joined by a young man with a pleasant face.

"Excuse me," he said, "but I believe you are Carson."

"Yes," I said.

"My name is Chapman. I am another assistant rep. There are two others, Daunon and Brick. You will meet them here tonight. We all congregate in the office and hand in the clients' excursion tickets. I suppose it's all pretty strange to you. What do you think of Box?"

"I don't know what to think," I replied.

"Did he tell you the police were after you, or that someone had rung up because a girl had jumped out of the window? That's what he said to me. He made one assistant rep put on an absurd green uniform, three sizes too small for him, and sleep in the lavatory. There was no other accommodation, he said. Make room for visitors, he said, they won't stay long."

Chapman strolled along with me to the Paradiso. "Box can't really speak a word of dialect. He made it up. The best thing he ever did was a week ago. An honest elderly couple arrived and went to see Box about their rooms, which had been booked at the Hotel Cosmos. He heard them out and then spoke to his clerk in dialect. 'I am very sorry,' he said, 'but there has been some mistake. At Head Office. There are no rooms here. You will have to go to a hotel on top of Mount

San Salvatore.' He pointed to that mountain up there. The clients looked terribly upset and asked how to get there. By bucket, Box told them. It hangs from a cable attached to the mountain top. I think they have strengthened it since the accident. It took them ten minutes to see the joke. Well, here's the Paradiso. Good luck."

It was a pleasant, informal hotel, and for a few days I had nothing much to do except greet new arrivals and collect excursion tickets. In the evenings I went round to the Cosmos, where I made friends with Daunon and Brick. Daunon had been in the French Resistance, and had a scar running down his face. He was very romantic and was always on the look-out for girls. He fell heavily in love with them and combed their hair for hours. Brick was more solid, a fair-haired man with a red face, but I could see that both of them had been corrupted by Box. They continually lied to the clients.

After a time I realised that the same clients came back year after year to be lied to. It was an art not only invented by Box but practised by the assistant reps, the hotel managers, and the fishermen on the lake. These fishermen already possessed a grain of fantasy, because when they wanted to insult each other they cried "Go away, Nose." The centre of lies was the lake itself.

Lake Lugano invites lies. It is beguiling and mysterious. It wears absurd clouds on the tops of its mountains. It has as many moods and dresses as a woman in love. It is inconsistent. It wanders in and out of Italy, touches on peculiar little republics, and back again. Opposite the town of Lugano, across the lake, is Campione, a few square miles of Italy entirely surrounded by Switzerland. It has its own police, postage stamps, and lives off the revenue of an enormous casino where you can lose your money at roulette, baccarat or chemin-de-fer. The lake twists about, and to the east passes Gaudria, a village built into the cliff, and once the resort of smugglers.

I went on my first excursion. Box coached me. The clients assembled at the little jetty by the Cosmos, and we all got into the launch. "This lake," said Box, "is bottomless. The villa we are passing on our left belongs to an Indian Rajah and is the scene of unspeakable orgies." He described some of them. The clients listened with rapt faces. I could imagine them during a freezing English winter, huddling round the fire and saying to each other, "I wonder how that Indian Rajah is getting on?" Box went on giving lurid descriptions of the other villas, and I began to get the gist of the thing.

The next time I went on the lake I gave a description of the enormous fresh-water sharks which were so intelligent that they could be harnessed to the fishing boats and which came up to be fed. Two old ladies had actually come down to the waterside with pieces of bread, waiting for them. Then there was the two-hundred-foot cliff which ran sheerly into the lake, from where former clients had dived for the Magic Carpets aquatic cup. And I invented a ghost which inhabited the woods of San Giorgio, behind a chalet where we called in for tea. An obliging boatman went behind a tree and howled.

There were other excursions, too, to St. Moritz, the Rhône Glacier, Milan, the Grande Chartreuse, and Pontresina. We all had our own techniques. When Daunon took the Rhône Glacier excursion, he used to wait until all his clients had entered the tunnel bored within the glacier and shout, "Look out, the ice is melting." He was very good at placating them afterwards and was a deservedly popular figure. One of the clients who came every year was a man called Towncroft who eventually inveigled his wife to Castagnuola and the Rhône Glacier. She died later of shock. Everyone said it was premeditated, but this story was probably originated by Box. I used to specialise in the St. Moritz excursion which climbed over the Maloja Pass and past the lake of S. Maria. It crossed the Italian border at a little village called Castasegua, where they made a cherry brandy so powerful that you could smell it in the valley three miles away. At first I used to sneak into the kitchen of the inn and drink a bottle of it with the maids—all food and drink, cigarettes and cigars are free to the courier—but later, out of self-defence, I reintroduced it to the clients. The results were excellent. Elderly English ladies danced in the street with Italians and Germans. The arrival of my coach in Castasegua was always an event for the inhabitants, who poured out of their houses to watch the cherry-brandy fiesta. My cargo was nearly always one of mixed nationalities, because Box lent me out to the bus company as a kind of international courier to translate lies into four different languages.

There was always a great deal of happiness in Castasegua, a sense of liberation and holiday. The paint on the houses was fresh and new, the air was sweet, and the sun came down like a master of the earth's revels.

All of us, the most absurd, the most exalted, loved each other. It is something, that sudden, effortless frontier love towards which intellectuals strive with agonies and self-reproaches. And on we drove through the flower-woven Engadine, past the glittering lakes, and sang. At St. Moritz, the passengers ate their sandwiches in a windy, deserted hotel, the winter scene of millionaire orgies, while I hid in the kitchen and discussed a heaped plate of chamois with the waiters.

One evening I walked into my room at the Paradiso and found a girl sitting on my bed. She sat there quite simply and appeared to have been waiting some time. She looked at me and gave me a shy and polite smile. "Good evening," I said. She said something in German, and kept looking at me. I remembered having seen her before in the dining-room. I know a few words in German, and we proceeded to have a ridiculous conversation. After a great deal of effort I discovered that she came from Basel. Not Basel Dorf, but Basel Land. "Ah," I said. "Basel Land. *Sehr gut.*" We looked at each other,

and then I touched her hand. She withdrew it, saying *"Doch!"*
I had been told that the Swiss use the word *"Doch"* to mean
either yes or no. It depended on the intonation. I listened carefully to her intonation but got nothing from it. We just sat
there, looking at each other. She seemed quite placid. Finally
I kissed her, and she pushed me away, saying *"Doch!"* insistently but softly. She became my mistress and I called her
Doch, and adored her. We never spoke to each other, except
when she said *"Doch"*; we just pointed at things, and drank
together and swam together and slept together. There were
never any misunderstandings or protestations. Everything
gets killed by words sooner or later. When she left to go back
to Basel, I saw her off at the station, and she waved to me and
said *"Doch."* A lot of the sun went out of the sky.

Box was indeed a strange man. It was impossible to know
what he was thinking. When any of the Magic Carpets clients
had finished their holidays, they came to say goodbye to him,
and they almost had tears in their eyes. Goodbye, goodbye,
Mr. Box, we will come back next year, we will come back
every year. Goodbye, said Box, goodbye, waving vaguely
and turning to say something to his clerk in dialect. Perhaps
he hated them. Perhaps that was why he was always pulling
their legs. Yet he gave them something inestimable. Something
they could never have got from Shilly-Chalet or any of the
other regimented Magic Carpets centres. After their holiday,
they even looked different. They all had the same sort of
Castagnuola face, just like the fisherman who cried "Go away,
Nose."

One evening Box took me out for a drink. He looked surprisingly old and sad. I had never seen him look like this before. He ordered whisky.

"I feel so lonely," he said. "Did you guess it?"

"No," I replied.

Then he suddenly told me about his life. During the war

he had been shipwrecked in the Indian Ocean with twelve other men on a raft. One by one, they had gone mad and drowned. All except one other man. "A homosexual," said Box, "the bravest man I ever knew. They used to call him Mignonette on the troopship." When a boat eventually discovered them, Mignonette jumped off the raft and had his leg bitten off by a shark. "We ended up in a Japanese hospital," said Box. "I was like a little hairless monkey, all withered up. I thought I was still on the raft and kept crying out for Mignonette. Eventually they put Mignonette into bed with me, and we clung together for ten days and nights." He took a drink of whisky.

"What happened to Mignonette?" I asked.

"He recovered. He got into trouble with a Japanese sailor. Incorrigible." Box was grinning at me, and his face had resumed the contours of a clown. I laughed, relieved it was a joke. It hadn't suited him to look like that. Like seeing one's favourite actor in a dressing-gown, ravaged with grief.

Soon it was time for me to leave Castagnuola. The season was over. Fog, dead leaves, and ennui faced me in London. I said goodbye to Box in just the same way as all the others had said goodbye, goodbye, I will be back next year. He pretended to cry, seized some flowers out of a Cosmos vase and gave them to me. Then I'm sure he forgot me. But a year later, in London, looking over some old newspapers, I came across Box's story about the shipwreck exactly as he had told it to me. And he had been decorated by the King.

UNO SCHERZO

Most of the couriers, including me, were paid off for the winter. Only a few old hands stayed on. Custer handled a few stragglers' parties until December, and then went on the Winter Sports run. One or two toured the Midlands giving Magic Carpets lectures. "Here is a typical happy carefree houseparty at Shilly-Chalet. On the left, Doris, Tom, Gerry and Stan. Here's Stan again full of holiday spirit. No, not that sort of spirit." Then there was a Portuguese called Minao who was in charge of the Magic Carpet Beaters, a group of permanent couriers who received Masonic, business and youth-club parties and took them round the British Museum. In the summer, Minao conducted the Italian party tours, the only Magic Carpets activity which seemed to hold endless possibilities for rackets and pleasure. He was the star courier, a large, clean-shaven man, almost completely bald, who had great success with women, and an unlimited capacity to swallow insults from clients. "The customer is always right," he said. Socially, by Magic Carpets standards, he was the equal of any representative. Even Mr. Tallport, the Paris representative, if he happened to be calling at the office, would make a point of saying good morning to him. "He's a bloody intriguer," Custer told me. "Watch out for him."

There I was back in London. I paid Mrs. Jerkin, my land-lady, a month's rent in advance, and she took me into her kitchen and gave me a cup of tea. Through the door a blowsy little garden leered at me. It served as opera-house, brothel, and lavatory for all the cats in Lupus Street. No flowers grew there. "Well," said Mrs. Jerkin. "Now you'll be settling down for a bit. You must be glad not to be flummox-ing about all over the place. Don't know how you can do it. Not at your age, I mean, you're not young any more. All right for young chaps to gallivant around. You should settle down and get married. Find a steady respectable job. I mean, you're educated and all that."

Next spring I was put on Italian tours. Italian party couriers travelled with a twenty-pound float in the form of travellers' cheques. This was generally spent by the courier himself, be-cause he settled personally with the Accounts Department when he came back, after making out an expense sheet. Grasp sent me off to Reservations to get the list of travellers. They were divided into first and second class—first- and second-class travel and hotels. All of them required special accommo-dation, single rooms with the best view and easy access to bathrooms. "Don't take any notice of that," said Grasp. "Just placate them. Most of them will sleep two or even three to a room. At the back. And, by the way, a chap called Brolio will meet you at Domodossola. He is the Italian tourist representa-tive."

"*È uno scherzo*" is Italian for "It's a joke."

The words tinkle now through the fog, the taste of Chianti is on my lips, the sunshine burns my back, the miraculous, the preposterous, the joke-like loom through the utility curtain. Above all they recall the large bland face of Signor Vittorio Brolio. Where are you now, Brolio, you who grow fatter as the days grow thinner, who laugh louder as others weep? I met Brolio at Domodossola. He stood on the platform, immense, wearing a blue gabardine suit, and shouted, "I am Vittorio Brolio." Who was I to know that he was the un-crowned king of Italy? I leant out of the railway carriage and shook his hand. He explained that he was the representative of the Italian Tourist Bureau and would accompany me all through Italy. Were there any beautiful women in the party? He glanced up and down the train and saw the edgy, over-night, tea-longing faces of my party, already wincing at the hot sun and the difference. They already disapproved. Perhaps they could hear, as I could, the far-off riot of the fauns chasing the nymphs over the hills, the winy belch of Bacchus in his Black Market fairyland. And here was the master of the revels himself, the arch-priest of the irresponsible sunshine, Vittorio Brolio.

I told him there were two young girls called Daisy and Milly. Nothing else was possible. What charming names, he said. Dizey and Meely. Did I want both of them? No, I said. Then which could he have? After reflection I gave him Milly. All through, our only quarrels were about Daisy and Milly. I had been seen with Milly in the Medici Chapel in Florence; I had seen Brolio with Daisy in the catacombs in Rome. They were our only human interests among the party.

Brolio hated tourists unless they were happy, rich or physi-cally attractive. Directly they started to complain he quivered with rage. He always seized an empty railway carriage (first class), labelled it "Office. Private" and pulled down the blinds. In this, from Stresa to Rome, from Rome to Naples, we sat with Daisy and Milly, even when the other carriages were bulging with broiled tourists drinking soda-water. At these times, Brolio resembled Nero. When a hovering, hot, frus-trated Thermos of a face appeared at the door he waved it away. It didn't live. I envied him. For me the Thermos faces lived, always had lived. A guilty social sense made me imagine a world fit for only the Thermos to live in, steadily rustling away beauty with huge paper bags.

In Stresa I first saw Brolio's power. He walked into my hotel and set the restaurant upside down, sending away every dish, receiving apologies from the head waiter. "*È uno scherzo*," he said, shovelling down the food and emptying the second bottle of wine. "They expect it, and while you eat with me you will eat the best, better than the tourist." When he spoke to the staff his face had a sudden absurd charm like an enormous, pampered child, and the girls giggled and did everything they could for him.

After lunch he went swimming in the lake. He lay down in the sun like a whimsical pink elephant, wearing a ridiculous white peaked cap he had bought in Capri. When he swam in the lake he puffed like a monster.

We took an excursion of our tourists to Isola Bella, where there is a palace and grounds which exhale a quite Victorian stuffiness. Brolio was only interested in securing commission from the stall-holders after our party had engulfed curios, sun-hats, bogus cameos and shawls. While the party were sweating through the palace he said: what about a *scherzo?* There were two pieces of venerable cannon standing outside the palace which had obviously not been moved for at least a hundred years. What about rolling these down to the lakeside and having a mock duel? This we did.

Our act caused a sensation. Officials poured out of the palace, and faces poured out of windows, shouting. We were surrounded. The situation was ugly. Brolio smiled his fat absurd sunflower smile and said "*È uno scherzo*." He opened his arms. *È uno scherzo*. The officials were immediately reassured. *È uno scherzo*. Life is real, life is earnest. *È uno scherzo*. Release the coloured balloons, here is the fat lord of misrule, blessed is the carnival. Brolio asked an official with a sword to take a picture of us with his camera. Then we went for a swim. "It is a beautiful life," said Brolio, his belly protruding like an island out of the water. "Are you happy?"

"Yes," I said.

"That is all that matters, my friend."

All through Italy Brolio dominated hotels, railway stations, banks. From far in the distance people could see him coming and cried *"Ma è Brolio"*—but it's Brolio—and the girls giggled and gorgeous officials bowed down to the ground. He ate and drank like a legend; he laughed until he quivered like a huge jelly; he shouted at tourists: "This carriage is private"; he played *scherzi* till the tears poured down his cheeks. In Capri he put me on a donkey and gave it a terrific slap on the rump which sent the animal flying into a fruit stall. Women screamed and people ran out of their shops. *"È uno scherzo,"* said Brolio, *"è uno scherzo."*

Brolio was highly efficient and very generous. He never took any commission for himself for excursions, he gave it all to me. He came to my hotel in the morning and handed out thousand-lira notes. This was small money, he said, not for him to sniff at. He was used to heiresses, rich women from America and Egypt who gave him their hearts and diamonds. He wasn't bragging like a mercenary from *Don Juan;* these women must have laughed affectionately at this garguantuan child with his peaked Capri hat. He was gross and greedy, but he was aware of the forms of slenderness. During a night train trip from Rome to Pisa he woke up Daisy and Milly and me, and pointed out of the window at moon-picked velvety ruins. "Poetry," he said. "For you."

Brolio amazed me most in Rome. Earlier in the trip he had suggested that we all had an audience with the Pope; he had said it casually and I had dismissed it. When we arrived in Rome, he rang me up and said the Pope would see us, would I get the party ready the next morning at nine o'clock. Fleets of coaches drove up to the hotels, the tourists were swept away to the Vatican. We waited for hours in the square of St. Peter's before Vittorio Brolio stepped out of a taxi, solemnly dressed in black, his bulk held in check, treading softly. Again officials came out to him, bowing. *"Ma è Brolio."* The Swiss guards gave him approving looks as he mounted the stairs, and turned to us with a magnificent gesture—come, follow. And we all trooped up the stairs after him and through the magnificent galleries until we came to the audience room. There Brolio lined us up against the walls as though we were about to be shot, looking so black and solemn that many tourists thought of escaping, but were too alarmed by the guards to try it.

After a time one of the doors opened, more guards and Vatican officials entered and then the Pope slipped simply in. He spoke to each one of us and blessed us, his face like a gentle and good autumn day. After the individual blessing, he gave us a collective blessing, and softly left the room. But, amazingly, he came back and I saw him talking to Brolio. Suddenly the Pope smiled and I knew Brolio had released a coloured balloon. Brolio was looking himself again, genial and irresponsible. The Pope came forward to us and put his arm round various shoulders. "Come, let us have our photograph taken together," he said. "Come along." And his expression seemed to say, let us have a *scherzo.*

THE GUIDES OF NAPLES

GRASP sent me off on the Italian tours again. "We've had some good letters about you," he said. "Quite a lot of bad. Apparently you're a bit rude. But the ones who liked you, liked you. This time the excursion covers Naples. There are about a hundred and twenty people. We're giving you two assistants. You'll need them."

He saw me off at the station. "Terrible-looking bastards," he said pityingly. "Why don't you get yourself a decent job?"

The Italians of the north start holding their noses when they go south of Rome and say "*ma sono barbari*," they are savages. Naples hums like bluebottles on a rotten plum, it smells of hot oranges and garlic, and the people shine like butter. Everybody shouts all the time, they lean out of the windows shouting out intimate details, and children burst into life like rockets. And they sing. They sing the same old songs over and over again, they sell you everything, they even sell you hope. In Naples nothing is sacred, nothing is trivial.

Again I met Brolio, and we proceeded on our journey downwards to Naples.

Outside Naples is an extensive excursion area, dreamy and

blue and golden, Pompeii, Sorrento, Amalfi, the island of Capri, Positano. Within this area is the fabulous cameo country, the El Dorado of couriers, guides, chauffeurs, vendors, and touts. It is the Mecca of the ten per cent. Numbers of cameo factories compete to make cameos as delicate as ferns, as creamy and rosy as a milkmaid's breast, tripping with goddesses and fauns. These go to the heads of tourists like wine, and absorb their travellers' cheques before they can filter through to silk scarves, rosewood cabinets or binges in Capri. A few years in Cameo land should enable the travel man to hibernate in Rome for the winter. If it wasn't for the guides of Naples.

The guides of Naples wear smart gabardine suits, have smiles like suns and sing. They are as fast as snakes. On our first visit to Naples they opened their arms like long-lost brothers, welcomed us to their hearts, and threw Naples, no, more than Naples, all the south, girls and wine and music, at our feet. They accompanied the tourists to Pompeii, one to each coach. I and my assistants collected tips for them (apart from the private gratuities conferred for showing rude pictures on the walls) and off we swept to the heart of Cameo land, to a selected factory. All the way there, while the coaches swished over the dusty roads, the guides talked about cameos. Hypnotically. Softly. With penetrating, mystic eyes they worked up a cameo lust. I could feel it myself. Everyone's hands were itching for cameos. Only the cameos of Cameo land, only the cameos of this particular factory . . . Cameos . . . Cameos . . . Cameos . . .

By the time we reached the factory the tourists rushed in and practically tore at the cameos with their teeth. They were beautifully arranged under glass cases, snowily chiselled myths on shell, unbearably tempting to the homespun hearts of the north, and many was the grey woman who heard the fairies singing and who reached for her wallet. Next to the showroom were the craftsmen, bent over their minute, frothy work. I hovered about in the background thinking of the commission mounting up and up, watching the wads of money changing hands. I could see myself renting a villa, buying a yacht. The glass cases were bare. Psyche and Cupid had fled. Aphrodite had been kidnapped for a soirée at Macclesfield. . . .

Probably these craftsmen absorbed in the minute sublimity of their work were underpaid, getting only a fraction of the amount taken by touts, agents, managers, publicity vultures, contact men and so on. But so it has always been since the world began. Men grow fat on Beauty without ever perceiving it, merely going by the rumour of it, being cunning and poker-faced, while the craftsmen (if they're not businessmen themselves) work at the behest of the Dream on starvation level. There's no trade union or welfare organisation for them. And in the black lands of the Midlands, over high tea, Peresphone will arise from the underworld on many an ample bosom and only arouse a slight curiosity and a blunt-thumbed handling.

Vittorio Brolio kept in the background and just gave me an occasional wink. He barely spoke to the guides at all. After all, he came from the north of Italy. He didn't consider the south even faintly civilised, though he was sensitive to the beauty of the cameos, but most Italians are alive to fine craftsmanship and take it for granted. Brolio had a liberal eye for women and an expensive taste in wines, so commission was his life-blood. He could hardly look at a beautiful mountain without thinking of commission, and the very sight of Pompeii made his fingers twitch with the longing to be able to sell it to rich Americans. One of the reasons why he despised the present party he was attached to was because they had so little basic currency, and none of the women was young or desirable.

I spoke to the head guide. What about the commission? He patted me on the back, smiled with brilliant teeth, flung Vesuvius, Herculaneum, Castellamare at my feet. Later. All would be arranged later.

The tourists tottered out of the factory plastered with cameos, the guides smiled their brilliant smiles and sang *Santa Lucia.*

> *Sul mare luccica*
> *L'astro d'argento*
> *Placida e londa.*

When I went up to them, they patted me on the back and said "Later. Later."

> *Prospero il vento . . .*

On to Sorrento. Sorrento. The guides were at the top of their form.

> *Questa terra di amore . . .*

Yes. Yes. Yes. Later. All will be arranged later.

> *Non da mi più tormento.*
> *Tornà a Sorrento.*

We climbed into our buses. The natural exuberant beauty of the surroundings had uplifted everybody, there was no reason for anyone to feel cross about anything. Tomorrow would be back to normal, not enough seats on the train, somebody losing their baggage, their hotel wasn't warned, they hadn't even time for breakfast, did we have to change, they had been told they didn't have time to change, could we go into another carriage, we don't like *that* family, didn't you say we could have the first sitting for lunch, we're starving, absolutely. But now we were all relaxed. There was a memory of sunshine and song and gold on the blue water, an uninhibited afternoon of Mediterranean holiday.

We returned to Naples in the electric cool of the evening. As we reached the outskirts of the town, before the shouting and the clanging began, I again approached the head guide. He was superbly affable and offered me a small black cigar. Everything will be all right, he said, stopping a song. Equal division is made. That is how Naples is, absolutely fair shares for all. The guides, the conductors, the drivers, the guides' benevolent society, the coach-drivers, co-operative and friendly fund, the Neapolitan tourist development widows' and orphans' fund, the couriers and so on and so on. I needn't worry you with the details. He opened his wallet, took out a thousand-lira note, slipped it into my hand, burst into song and jumped off the coach. It was a ridiculously small sum. I waved it at him through the window. He waved back, smiling. Later, he shouted, all will be arranged later.

I told Brolio and Brolio swore, borrowing from many dialects, including the Tuscan. Barbarians. He would find a way. He would have a plan by the time I came back to Italy with my next party.

I returned to England. I hung around Victoria at the dead end of my heart, longing for cypresses and Campari and shouting copper voices. That is the trouble about being a courier. You start to live in two or three countries at once. You wake up in the morning, open your eyes and wonder where you are. In a train near the Swiss frontier? In a hotel in Montparnasse? If you go to the window will you see the Grand Canal in Venice all silver in the early morning? No, it's just the Vauxhall Bridge Road with the trivial squeaking trams going past the fly-blown newsagents and the bleary cafés, and you begin to long for the poetry of the Italian streets and shouting Naples, all the superstitions and the squalor and the deep crystalline happiness of the south. Yes, at the price of conducting the most tiresome, tiring, complaining parties of tourists that exist in the world, I wanted one foot in the slums of Naples.

Eventually a new party was made up, one hundred and ten of them, and I checked their names with the Italian Tourist Office and collected the collective tickets and all the passes and the meal coupons, and set off for Victoria–Dover–Calais –Paris–Vallorbe–Brigue–Domodossola and Stresa. I say, courier, there are too many people in our carriage, when do we have lunch, little Albert feels queer, my husband says he must have some soda-water.

Domodossola. And there was Brolio waiting for me on the platform. He rushed to me with an exultant cry, the cry of a very fat general confident before bloody battle. He had evolved a master plan. We were going to cut the guides of Naples out of the picture. Obliterate them. We could go to the factories alone and collect our ten per cent. Then we would hibernate for the winter like Doges.

From Rome we telephoned to the Tourist Bureau in Naples and told them to dismiss the guides allotted to our excursions. The manager explained that this was not possible because they were official accredited guides with diplomas. He enlarged on their heredity, health and moral code, and sketched their future. The manager compromised and said that we could dismiss them after the visit to Pompeii. They must handle Pompeii. It was the vital point gained. We could continue to the cameo factory alone.

When we arrived in Naples, the guides were waiting for me at my hotel. They had heard of the plan. But when I say "guides" I do not mean the same guides. Each face was a new face, wreathed in innocent smiles, each hand grasped mine in honest comradeship. We are not taking you beyond Pompeii, I said. But there was a mistake, they said, weaving about me, it was all a hideous mistake. We are new guides, official guides with real diplomas. We are not like the other dishonest guides with forged diplomas who behaved so monstrously. All Naples spits at them. They have been deported. You can trust *us* completely. Take us with you. We will give you *more* than your share. The matter is ended, I said.

So they only came as far as Pompeii in the motor coaches. They guided my hundred and ten clients around the ruins, and when the visit was over, I stayed behind to collect the stragglers. As I strolled back to the entrance I saw Brolio running towards me waving his arms. "The swine," he shouted, and broke off into Umbrian. "They've done it again. Look for yourself." He dragged me down towards the coaches.

The whole area was crammed with cameo-sellers. Crippled cameo-sellers, one-eyed cameo-sellers, fat, thin, ragged, tall, short, holding their trays up to the tourists in the coaches. The cameos were selling like hot cakes. They melted away like ice in the sun. The guides told the tourists they were the best cameos in Italy. Brolio told me the best were all made in my Birmingham. They rounded up all the vagrants they could get. The tourists would have no more money left when they got to the factory.

"No commission," I said.

"No commission," shouted Brolio, and added something in Ligurian.

"No commission," I repeated, and looked at Brolio's red face. Then suddenly we started to laugh; we couldn't stop laughing. The tears rolled down our cheeks. Our laughter seemed to act as a signal to the guides, who had hidden themselves behind trees or peeped over windowsills. They all burst into song and surged forward. Not only the new guides but the old guides too. The sun was shining. Their arms were open. "Come and let's drink together," they said. So we drank. And when they said goodbye, they were still laughing, and there were tears in their eyes.

THE CAPOGRUPPO

THIS IDYLLIC EXISTENCE in Italian tours did not last. The numbers of the clients rose from 30 to 100 and finally to 250. I began to feel I was managing a sort of perambulating factory, and it didn't suit me at all.

My last Italian tour took place in a warm, hazy autumn. I should have learnt my lessons, but that is something I never do. All the Magic Carpets Italian tours were divided into first- and second-class bookings, which included first- and second-class accommodation on the trains and in the hotels. This arrangement always caused a certain amount of bad feeling, since almost all Magic Carpets clients belonged to the same social stratum; and, if anything, the second-class group contained more schoolmasters, pianists and pretty girls than the first. It was generally understood, as an unwritten law for tour couriers, that they should always choose their girl-friends from the second-class group—even though the chief courier (or *Capogruppo*, as he was called in Italy) stayed in first-class hotels and was fed personally with peaches and cream by the *maître d'hôtel* himself. Once over the Italian frontier, among the golden flowers, dirt, shouts, and sly nymphs of that black-market fairyland, the *Capogruppo* could install his second-class girl in his hotel for the evening and could fear nothing worse than first-class winks in the bar and applause from the waiters.

For my last tour, although there was a very large number of clients, I was furnished with only one assistant courier. He was a young man called Bill Yates, and was an out-of-work comedian who had just finished a season in Burnley. Bill Yates started joking the moment I met him at Victoria Station and continued all the way to Paris, where we changed trains to re-embark on the midnight special to Stresa. It was at this moment that the tour began to disintegrate. For some reason or other I had acquired last year's time-table and was unaware that the Stresa train was, in fact, due to leave an hour earlier than usual. We were sitting in the station restaurant, and Bill Yates was going around the tables telling dubious jokes, when a waiter happened to mention the time of the train. It was leaving in exactly three minutes.

I jumped up, grabbed Yates by the arm and told him to get everyone out on to the platform immediately. After he had finished laughing, we rushed all over the restaurant, shouting at Magic Carpets clients, French commercial travellers, Swiss diplomats, *poules de luxe*, and elderly ladies going for the cure. Then we rushed down to the conveniences, which, for some psychological reason or other, are more frequently used by Magic Carpets tourists than any other class of human being, and banged on the doors. "Platform Five," we shouted. "The train is leaving in one minute."

The confusion on Platform Five was quite frightening. Several people were actually crying, suitcases were lost, wives were shouting for their husbands, the train whistle blew, there was even some sort of fight going on near the engine. Desperately I bribed one of the station officials, who stopped the fight and delayed the departure of the train. Yates went around telling jokes, but in the end even he got alarmed, and both of us cleared off, leaving the chaos to be unravelled by the station official. We were slinking down a first-class corridor when we saw a very smart, youngish woman sitting in one of the compartments doubled up with laughter.

"May we come in?" said Yates. "We want to hide, as a matter of fact."

"By all means," said the woman.

We arranged our luggage and sat down facing her. When we explained what had happened, she started laughing all over again.

"I'm sorry," she said, "but I happen to be one of your clients. I've come all the way from America."

"I'm sorry," I said.

"That's all right," she said. "This makes a great change from America."

After a few minutes, Bill Yates left the compartment to comb the train for a girl and to make a few experimental jokes. He returned later with a young woman with reddened eyes, who told us she couldn't find her father. "He'll turn up," said Yates. "It isn't as bad as parts of the last war."

The situation was bad. The *Capogruppo* has to keep some sort of moral ascendancy—the temperature of the tour must be kept constant. I had at the very beginning of the fortnight lost control, and it needed a brilliant stroke indeed to win back supremacy. But I could not envisage such a stroke. I suspect that many defeated generals have fallen back on love as an escape from their predicament, and I was no exception. The American girl, Leonora, at once cast her silver chains over me, and all that I knew of Italy was hers. Hers and nobody else's. So it was not surprising that I made the second fatal mistake before the train reached Stresa. I completely forgot to allocate hotels, first- and second-class; and as soon as all the clients had been deposited on the platform, luggage was whisked away indiscriminately, and more agonising bedlam followed.

But all was not lost. The wayward wand of Italy always performs its own kind of careless magic; and in the morning, under a dancing sun, nearly all the tourists had forgotten the horrors of the night before. This should have been my cue to start hunting for a second-class girl. But I didn't. I stuck to Leonora, swimming with her on the private beach outside the huge, idyllic hotel, guiding her through the hideous palace on Isola Bella and, in Venice, mooning through the dappled canals by gondola. It was open rebellion against the code. Leonora was aware of this and began district-visiting in an eager American way, spending a lot of time in the second-class hotels where we nearly always ate our meals. But it was no good. "Showing off, that's what she's up to," I heard a woman say to her husband half-way across the Bridge of Sighs. Even the *maître d'hôtel* at the Grand tried to convince me of my mistake. "You'll regret this in Capri," he said.

From now on the suspicious clients held me personally responsible for every disaster that happened. An old gentleman was run over in Rome, and I received threatening letters. It rained heavily in Capri, and I was cut dead. The train was an hour late returning to Venice, and there was a minor revolution at the railway station.

Even Yates's stock of jokes ran very low. At last, on the day after our arrival in Venice, he told me he had seen Leonora leaving the room of the *maître d'hôtel* at three o'clock in the morning. I did not speak to her again until we arrived back in Victoria Station.

"Please believe me," she said, "I did it entirely for you."

That didn't stop me getting the sack.

PART TWO

⎍⌐⎍⌐⎍⌐⎍⌐⎍⌐⎍⌐⎍⌐⎍⌐⎍⌐⎍⌐

LOOKING FOR A BANDIT

A MAGAZINE once sent me to Sicily to find a bandit. Or rather, I insinuated to the magazine that they might send me. I wanted to get miles away from Bayswater: people were dying in the hotels, and there was a feeling of crumbling masonry. The bandit was a good bet; he stirred in the dreams of wives, boxed-up men in sharp collars, numbered people and drugged people. You could think of him as you thought of a secret seaside place. I flew to Palermo. The heat was like a thick blue blanket; and after getting myself a room I sat drinking glasses of Campari and sweating. Then I drove around the city in a horse-carriage. All towns are fairly alike; there are trams and taxis, coiffeurs and policemen. Obviously nobody was even *thinking* about a bandit. I felt suddenly naïve after all that scientific urgency in aeroplanes. It was a relief to see a flock of goats padding timelessly past an enormous bank and turning into a dark street of shouts and washing. Perhaps something *could* happen here.

I asked the driver to take me to the offices of the *Giornale di Sicilia*. The horse mystically trotted all around Palermo to get there, and I learnt later that all the Palermo horses do this. It is always four hundred lire. I went into the office of the

Giornale, met the editor and announced that I had come about the bandit. He laughed a great deal, but quite politely, and told me there were hundreds of journalists in Palermo who had come about the bandit. Many of them were neurotic ladies. One elderly one had actually disrobed herself in a public fountain. Another had apparently slept with this delinquent and written an absurd book. The *Giornale* always kept a whole front page to describe the astonishing antics of bandit-hunting foreigners. They were the talk of the town. What did it all mean? How strange must be our foggy democracies. The civilization and culture of Sicily, the cathedral, churches and gardens of the city were of absorbing interest. There was a hydro-electric scheme. There was a *Concurrenza di Bellezza,* a Beauty Competition . . .

"That is the way it is," I said lamely. "I have come about the bandit. Personally." I looked at the editor with the eyes of civilization, almost with the eyes of his cathedral.

"Well," he said, "there is the Rome correspondent of *Domani.* His name is Rocca. He lives at the Hotel Paloma. He may help you."

I knew about Rocca. His stories about the bandit were quite sensational and formed the source of most of the items published in European newspapers. Robin Hood, disguises, armed uprisings, and so on. I drove to the Hotel Paloma. All around Palermo by the horse's mystic circle. Four hundred lire. "Yes. Signor Rocca is on the roof garden. He will see you." I shot up by lift. Signor Rocca rose from a table. He was dressed in shorts, khaki shirt, hobnailed boots, and wore a sort of hunting-knife at his belt. He was bronzed and bearded. "Have a drink," he whispered. "I can help you. Tomorrow. I have just returned from the mountains. Exhausted." He passed a weary hand over his forehead. He exhaled an atmosphere of dust, mountains and vermouth. I felt completely inexperienced beside him. He had already written forty-six articles on this bandit, had lived six months in Sicily and libelled nearly everybody of any importance. He was a man of civilization and earned a living at words. I, on the other hand, was lucky to get an article about a pelican in a woman's magazine. "Tomorrow," he repeated.

Next I went to see the British Consul. He was a charming, elderly man who immediately began to tell me about his mother's enormous garden. After that he gave me a theory that the bandit was a Scottish army deserter; some tartan had been discovered in a cave. "Also the way the man shoots," said the Consul. Then I mentioned Rocca to him. The Consul laughed. "Oh, old Rocca," he said. "On that roof garden. He's never left it, you know. Except to go to bed." He gave the sort of laugh the British accord to enterprising natives. "Got to admire him in a way. And, incidentally, you'd better get a bandit card from the police."

I went to the police headquarters and they roared with laughter. "Do *we*," they asked, "fly all the way to *your* country to see *your* robbers?" But they gave me a limited authorisation to look for bandits. As I left, a van drew up, a door opened, and a distinguished manacled man stepped out. Later I learnt that he was the correspondent of the ——. I then tried to get in touch with the military. They told me the police permit was quite useless, since the police were not in charge of bandits any more. So two ways were left to me. One was the way of the barbarian, wandering about the wild mountains and asking for bandits. But I remembered the correspondent of the —— stepping out of the van. Also, although I am entirely uncivilised, or for this very reason, I wished to appear urbane and be well spoken of by the *Giornale di Sicilia*. The other way was to wear shorts and join Rocca on his roof garden. That was too sophisticated and I am bad at inventing. So I went to the *Concurrenza di Bellezza* and became British Representative, wearing a rather dirty gabardine suit.

I had the feeling that Palermo had held this Beauty Competition for thousands of years. The saxophones sobbed over the sea. The moon spun. Girls in bikinis minced across a ramp, cameras clicked, and satyrs in evening dress with matted hair under their shirt-fronts charged forward. A kind of comedian-floorwalker remonstrated with them through a loudspeaker, reminding them of the hydro-electric scheme, and that they were civilized. The landowners sat still as lizards, their lust under perfect control, their women ivory white and contemptuous, ear-dropped with cold diamonds. "Gentlemen," cried the comedian-floorwalker, "we have a world-famous cathedral, churches and gardens. *Please* leave the girls' fannies alone." In the distance I could often see the really wondering faces of the poor. They had probably always connected rows of beautiful girls with miracles. Or there was the hope.

While I was watching all this, I met a woman journalist from England. She was intensely busy, practical, vivacious and business-like. She was running a series of articles for press networks all over the world on the Girls, the beauties of Nature, clothes and recipes of all nations. Also folk-dancing and Youth organisations. "Now then," she said to me, over the glass of champagne, "tell me about the bandit."

It was the champagne that did it. "I have just returned from the mountains," I said.

HOW I NEARLY BECAME AN M.P.

WHEN I WROTE for this magazine which no longer exists, I wrote about travel agencies and folk-dancing. One day I was sitting in the office, sniffing around for money, when the Features Editor called me in.

"Listen," he said, after a slight bark, "what about politics?"

"What about politics?" I repeated.

"I mean for you," he said, flashing his spectacles at me like a doctor.

"I don't know anything about politics," I said. In fact I hardly knew anything about anything. Machines or women or cricket or economy. I could speak bad French and play the castanets.

"That's just the point," said the Features Editor. "Ignorance can be rather beautiful. You approach the whole problem with freshness. Disarming. Like a sort of Primitive. Sit down."

I sat down, and he handed me a pamphlet.

"Now then," he continued, "there's a General Election coming on and we propose sending you to Reading to test the atmosphere. Reading is a sort of electoral barometer, because every kind of Englishman is supposed to live there—people who make biscuits and bicycles, and students and re-

tired colonels and grocers and burglars. Does it interest you?"
I pondered the idea of Reading. All I really wanted was to
fly back to Sicily, but that was obviously out of the question.

"There will be beer money," said the Features Editor, fingering some pound notes.

I took the train to Reading, and wandered about the streets
for a time, thinking how alike all English towns are, with
chemists, tea-rooms, cats in windows, and armies of prams.
Then I entered a few public houses, partly to effect an emotional short-cut into the General Election complex, partly to
quench my thirst, and partly to summon up enough courage
to face the different Party Headquarters. I began with Labour.
Their headquarters were in a Working Men's Institute, and
were as solid as treacle pudding, with billiards and darts and
shirt-sleeves and sturdy bewildered pipes.

"It's going to be a stiff fight," said an official, puffing hon-
estly at me and handing me a pint.

"Why stiff?" I asked.

"Because they don't play fair," said the official. "They don't
care about truth, and they hit under the belt. It's easy to talk
about bacon and fish and all that sort of thing, and merely pull
wool over people's eyes. You see, people don't think."

He handed me another pint. I could see he was a nice man
who wouldn't weave spells with bacon and fish.

"You say 'they'," I said. "Are you including the Liberals?"

He suddenly looked at me with astonishment and splut-
tered into his beer. "What?" he cried.

"The Liberals," I repeated. I felt I had used a filthy word.

"But they're hopeless," he cried. "Forget about them.
They're like lemonade at the vicarage. Like a toy pistol. Don't
you know there's a war on? Mind you, I've nothing against
them. The Liberal tradition is enormously important. In fact
all of us here would be Liberals if it wasn't for the Tories."

My next call was at the Conservative Party Headquarters.

The agent was a youngish man who made me think, somehow, of Bulldog Drummond. His room was full of maps and diagrams and flags and memoranda. "It's going to be a fight," he said, "but we'll win." He looked supremely confident, bouncing and fit. "We know their tricks," he continued. "I've studied them some time. A foxy lot, dodgy as hell, but we'll thrash them." I had the impression, here in this room, that I was with some sort of District Commissioner far in the depths of Africa. Outside were the natives waving spears.

"What about the Liberals?" I asked the Commissioner.

"Liberals," he cried with a shout, "forget all about them, my friend. Mere fly-paper. Leaking hot-water bottles. Ineffectual vote-splitters. Mind you, I've nothing against them. The Liberal concept is quite magnificent. In fact we'd *be* Liberals ourselves if it wasn't for that Labour crowd."

After another drink I went to look for the Liberal candidate, a Mr. Fletcher. For some reason he was in a printing house. He was a young man with a moustache and a background of subdued laughter.

"This is really a Liberal town," said Fletcher, "and I don't see why I shouldn't have a shot at it. Do you?"

"No," I said.

"What are your political views?" he asked.

"I don't know," I said, "but I feel Liberal."

"I see," he said. Liberal, after all, was a wonderful portmanteau word into which you could cram love, wines, guilt, and loans. "Come and stay a few days at my house in the country" he said, "and then you can watch the electoral machinery at work."

I stayed at his house, which was charming, and met his father. His father was a man glued to his library, except when he stood at the open windows listening to the birds. On the first morning, after breakfast, he took me aside and begged me to try to influence his son against entering politics. "So extremely vulgar," he said, "like the theatre." I promised I would try, but obviously young Fletcher was an idealist like his father, only much more flippant. We drove into Reading and had a loudspeaker fixed above the car.

"The electrician is a keen Liberal," said Fletcher, introducing me to a young thin man with keen Liberal eyes. We sat in the car inventing speeches, and the absurdity of election time suddenly gripped us. "What have you to gain from a Conservative victory?" said Fletcher in a vote-catching voice, addressing an imaginary audience. "People of Reading, consider this question carefully. You have nothing to gain but your chains, misery, despair, starvation and the workhouse. People of Reading, shut your ears to their fine promises which cover nothing less than a deliberate return to the Dark Ages. Save your women and children—and the aged. Vote Liberal."

"People of Reading," I cried, "what awaits you if Labour triumphs? This beautiful city will be ruled by a gang of upstart biscuit-mixers and bicycle-bevellers. Your churches will be razed to the ground, your libraries pillaged, your daughters raped. Blood will run in the gutters."

"For God's sake!" hissed a voice at the car window. It was the electrician, white as a frenzied monk. "The loudspeaker's on. Full strength. We were testing. There's a huge crowd at the street corner." He looked at Fletcher with miserable astonishment, like a devoted pupil who finds his master standing on his head. We turned around and saw the crowd. They seemed to be moving towards us, and I suddenly understood about election fever. Apart from stock jokes, it couldn't be tampered with. Hurriedly we drove off.

"That was quite a good speech," said Fletcher, slowing down a bit. "Would you like to stand for a constituency?"

THE BLESSING OF THE SEA

"Go to Hastings," said my Editor, and I got on a train. After Eastbourne, the train skirted the shore, and there were the waves bringing a pang of holidays and piers and buckets. At Hastings, the sea which was to receive its yearly Blessing looked green-cold, shrewish and unblessable, like a woman after a long quarrel. I made for the Old Town, passing through the anonymous seaside streets of stores and red-faced hotels, stark with fresh air, surrounded by fish-restaurants which became less and less refined until they stated openly "Frying today." Finally I was there, in a welter of winding streets and alleys, topped by the green dome of East Hill, where the cliff-funicular has a station like a renovated Norman castle.

The Procession of the Blessing started from St. Clement's Church off the High Street at seven o'clock in the evening. I slipped into the church and waylaid the rector. "There's always been some sort of Blessing here from the Lifeboat," he said; "it stopped during the war, but I got it going again. Of course there are many other Blessings down the Channel." I had a vision of the green, implacable sea wooed by Hymns Ancient and Modern all along the Channel coast.

131

Down by the Lifeboat house, a crowd was already collect-
ing, crunching the pebbles round the loudspeaker; the
Lifeboat collection box was clinking around, and the uniformed band of Hastings and St. Leonards were unpacking
their instruments. For some reason or other the flock was surrounded by policemen. It seemed unnecessary. The people
were quiet and expectant, so close to the cold sea, to the seagulls, and the ranks of fishing-boats. In front of us were the
black net-stores, like tall windows in mourning, behind us the
cold comfort of a dead fun-fair. But the sea was stronger and
colder than all this. I spoke to a fisherman. "Not what it was,"
he said. "We get the fish in the winter, but we can't sell it.
Plenty of fish. Lovely place." He spread out his hands. "It's
no good till the tourists come. And then there's fewer fish."
An old man, grafted on to his stick, looked up from under his
cap. "The fishermen here are dying out," he said; "can't give
us the big families any more. Not like the Peters and the
Adamses. And this is a bad sea here." He lifted his stick to the
gleaming modernistic lifeboat. "The Blessing's no joke, mister.
And I'll tell you something else. Soon as the Blessing's over,
there'll be a gale. It's the same every year."

The procession now wound down the High Street. Choris-
ters, clergy, crucifix rampant, a swarm of green-shirted wolf-
cubs. The rector and two curates climbed into the boat and
tinkered with the microphones. "Them things always go
wrong," murmured the old man. "They should shout. Same
thing to the sea." Hymn sheets were distributed, and the band
blew. "Oft in danger, oft in woe, Onward Christians, onward
go . . ." The old people sang, the young watched, children
played tag among the monolithic policemen. The rector had
the sea on his left hand, St. Clement's on his right, the crowd
before him—all these people, with the sea in their nerves. It
was Rogation week, the period of the Church's supplication
for the fruits of the land and sea. It was also the rector's

chance to spread the gospel, send up the rockets of Life in Death, Death in Life—to a congregation met together for magic. Following the hymn, a lesson was read—the miracle of the fishes and Christ walking on the sea. Then "Eternal Father, strong to save . . . O hear us when we cry to Thee for those in peril on the sea." This was the heart of the matter. Economics had twisted the blessing for abundance, which the rector now gave, lifting up his hand to consecrate the waters. Farther and farther from his congregation's elemental preoccupation went his fishing for souls, his boats and storms as symbols for the conquest of sin. The band bellowed "Pull for the shore, sailor, pull for the shore . . . Leave the poor stranded wreck and pull for the shore . . ."

All over Europe the fishermen were placating their enemy. Here, in Hastings, holiday-makers would swallow perhaps the Christian bait, refuse the Pagan magic. But not so the Old Town's fishermen: they were too close to the savagery of the sea. When the service was over and the crowd dispersed, the old man in the cap tapped me on the shoulder. "D'you see?" he said triumphantly. "The wind is rising."

CALLING BILL WOOLL

I WENT to Bertram Mills's Circus three days before the opening. I stood near the ring. Men were shovelling out sawdust,
and seamstresses stitched strips of the canopy which careered
down like rigging on a vast pleasure barge. High up in a neon-
lit eyrie was the bandstand; they were playing a fox-trot.
"For the sea-lions," said my guide, Mr. Walker. "They need
exact tempo, and one of them plays a mouth-organ. No,
they're not here yet. Which reminds me . . ." He struck his
forehead. "The fish . . ."
"What fish?" I asked.
"One moment."
Olympia rattled and thumped with hammers and drills, and
from the distance came echoes of caged African thunder. Suddenly two horses plunged among the measuring men and the
ringmaster and the carpenters, and capered in the ring, curv-
ing necks like breaking rollers. One of them lay on its back,
and the other jumped over it, backwards and forwards in time
with the sea-lion song. Nobody paid any attention to them. A
man sawed through a plank; someone shouted at the bandmas-
ter; a woman walked straight through the ring with a sheaf of
papers. The horses left. I asked a man in riding breeches about

134

them, but he hadn't seen them. "Probably the Radios," he said. "Remote control horses. Do you know a chap called Bill?"

"Bill who?" I said.

"Bill Wooll—the Staff Manager. Everybody's looking for him."

Walker reappeared. "Ah," said the man in riding breeches, "have *you* seen Bill? Fattini's swaypole's too high for the foundation. Those were his Milan measurements. Then there's the three ropes for the sky cyclists. And the sawdust."

"I want Bill," said Walker, "about the fish."

We wandered out of the ring, through the galleried stables and the clowns' dressing-rooms. Palomino horses stood in their makeshift beauty parlours, twitching cosseted tails. Shetlands tossed manes in miniature feuds. We opened a dressing-room door. On the dressing table lay a false nose, a child's Disney bucket, wooden dumb-bells. An Admiral's hat, a top hat and a dunce's cap hung from pegs. There were three trunks, each in diminishing size, marked with the names— ALBY, BEPPO, LITTLE BILLY. Outside the door was a tin cannon. At that moment a thin, melancholy man entered the room. "I am Alby," he said sadly. "Come to the canteen and meet Beppo and Billy."

We sat in the canteen drinking tea. Beppo was athletic and good looking; Little Billy a mannikin. "I used to be with Johnny Weismuller," said Beppo gloomily, "diving from eighty-five feet into tanks." He took a sip of tea. "In flames," he added.

Little Billy nodded solemnly. "I was one of Snow White's seven dwarfs," he said. "One night the chaps threw me into the girls' dressing-room. I was stark naked." He eyed me grimly and pointed a finger at my notebook. "Don't tell them where."

Then they discussed clowning technique. "We build it up out of ordinary situations," said Billy. "We cook up a sort of story and let it expand as it goes. Kind of telepathy. That's the basis of our humour." He stared unhappily at his tea.

"Even when it gets grotesque," said Alby. "For instance, take the awkward waiter situation. A few years ago I waited on four sea-lions and an elephant." He seemed near tears. The three looked at me from a clown's planet of despair. I rose from the table. "Knee and ankle trouble—that's the worst part," said Alby.

I came back to Olympia the next morning. The sawdust twinkled like a seaside holiday and the canopy shone in the firmament. The band was playing *La Comparsita*. Out of the loudspeaker crackled a voice—"Calling Bill Wooll. Will Bill Wooll report to Mr. Cyril!"

"Excuse me," said a voice, "would you mind moving a little." An axe flashed through the air and bit into a blackboard three feet away. It was Frank Foster, Joint Ringmaster, keeping his eye in. I ran and bumped into Walker.

"How are the fish?"

"We've got the fish," he said, "but there aren't any sea-lions. Have you seen Bill? You'd better come and see the cats." We walked through the gallery past a notice screaming NO SMOKING in four languages, and ending in a Chinese ideogram. We came out into a silent world of giant unpacked tows—the unborn Fun Fair. WOULD YOU LIKE TO BE AN AIR GUNNER? asked a placard. A mystic lady in a fur coat arranged press cuttings in front of a refined booth labelled OCCULT PARLOUR.

"Here are the cats," said Walker, "and there's Alexander Kerr in the cage."

The enormous circular cage housed four lions and two tigers. It was sly with the fug of dens. In the centre stood Alexander Kerr, the trainer, holding a whip and wheedling with the voice and expression of a schoolmaster, a lover or a missionary. "Sita! Sita! Sita!" he called. The tone trickled into the

136

angry heart of the tiger. Streamlined with hate, it fizzled, boiled and exploded in a roar, then looked uncertain like a woman who has said too much. Two lions yawned. Next the cage stood a morbid grey plaster house named "YE HAUNTED CASTLE." The door opened and a man came out, waved to somebody inside, ran down the steps and paused by the gate, looking for something in his pocket. I imagined a key, or a suburban railway ticket. But he brought out a screwdriver and got to work on the hinges. Finally Alexander came out. The class broke up, and the cats ran off. Alexander is a slight, slow-moving man with the shadows of cats in his eyes. He slouches easily, like a sailor or a cowboy, but he is wary in a long world of claws. "You can see cats thinking," he said. "I don't mind those cats, but they're giving me bears. Lions, tigers and bears! Bears are sods. Their eyes tell you nothing and their bite is blue murder. Come along to the zoo."

The zoo contained lions and tigers, a dromedary, a llama, monkeys, birds and a troupe of elephants. A lady painter was sketching the llama as we arrived. It suddenly bent its head down, seized the drawing-book in its teeth and began eating it. The elephants swayed from side to side, facing their striped enemies, their small eyes twinkling with antediluvian jokes. It was bath time. A taggle of wild boys brushed, scraped, pounded and mopped hides, pads and trunks. All the time they kept singing of Glasgow. Now and then an elephant (perhaps after a year's reflection) misbehaved. Then a wild boy, jumping on a polite trunk, screamed obscenities into one hypocritical eye. Alexander had gone into a tiger's cage and was having a scene with it. They were pommelling each other like private brothers. It was over in a moment; the tiger put on a popular face; a collar was slipped round its neck, and it was let out of the cage and strolled over to me and a couple of feuding photographers. "To get used to the place," said Alexander.

Walker appeared again. "The sea-lions are here," he said,

"someone heard them barking. But Bill's had the fish moved. Come and meet Amleto Sciplini—chimp act."

We walked back to the ring where a general rehearsal was starting. Already there was a horses' ballet and Coco the clown was trying out his nine-pound boots. "Terrible weight," said Coco; "I've little ones made for my grandchild—he's going to be a great clown. Seven years old now and he started at three. Pity he's the only genius out of nine . . ."

Amleto was sitting at the ring-side and breathed the Via Veneto, Caffè Espresso and Campari. "My chimps look like lovable children," he said, "but they are mean and moody. I tell everybody—'do not touch.' They need great discipline. The comedy? They have made it all themselves from their bad manners. Each time they make a new scene the people laugh and in it goes. But, my God, I can never be away from them—never!" We thanked Amleto and went to look for the sea-lions.

We found a van, peered through the mesh and saw the pseudo-scholarly eyes of a chimp. We heard barking, but it was a performing dog. Eventually we discovered Armand Guerre, the trainer, putting fish in a bucket. "Meet the sea-lions," he said, pointing towards his van. I climbed into a room like a cabin. At one end was darkness and a sound of hectic holiday splashing, passionate barks and a strong smell of herring. Dimly I could see three eager snake heads, twining in love knots. "Lights have fused," said Armand. "Has anyone seen Bill?" He began feeding his family. "They're four years old; begin training at two. These come from California—you can hear the American accent." His wife had an American accent, too, but she came from the Midlands. . . .

The next day was the full dress-rehearsal. The band played and in came the grand parade of horses, the fairy coach, the elephants, the Cobinas, the comedy cyclists and all the performers, and finally Alexander and his tiger. An explosion of clowns and the red-nosed charivari began. The chimpanzees played jazz, the elephants waltzed, Beppo began to perform a strong-man act with rubber weights, the sea-lions juggled and the canopy danced in a scream of children. "God Save the Queen" rolled on the audience, the fallen programmes, the trodden sawdust, and fountained to the smoky canopy. Soon there was emptiness. A distant elephant trumpeted, then silence.

A man came running across the ring and pushed his face near a microphone—"Calling Bill Wooll! Calling Bill Wooll!"

FALSE PRETENCES

FROM LES-SAINTES-MARIES I went to Arles and I went on an excursion. In the excursion-coach all my fellow-tourists were French, except for a young Canadian with an expensive camera. "I'm going around Europe," he told me, "but so far I find it disappointing."

On the seat next to me was a bright-eyed lady of middle-age who lived in Lyons. She was eager to talk. "I am a widow, and have been left a small business," she explained. "It is in the hands of a capable manager, so I enlarge myself by *tourisme*. In Perpignan I have done ten excursions. I feel I know the Pyrenees. What excursions have you been taking?"

I told her I had been living with gypsies in the Camargue.

"The gypsies?" she said. "I envy you; I am such a gypsy myself." She looked neat, clean, alert and business-like.

The bus set off. First we visited the ruined monastery of Montmajour. "Founded by the Benedictines," said Madame Pinaud, the excursionist. "I know much of this order. Do not pay too much attention to the guide. She is not certain of her facts."

The Canadian tried to take some photographs, but gave it up. "Light's poor in these places," he said gloomily, repacking his instrument. Then Fontville and the windmills of Alphonse Daudet. The sun wasn't behaving well, and the Canadian got rather cross. "This is the darndest windmill," he said. Yet one could have written happy, uncomplicated letters from such a mill, looking down on a valley smiling with dreamy shadow-play: it was one of those moments when one regrets whole areas of life.

Madame Pinaud asked the curator a host of questions. Did Daudet live in the windmill and work the machinery himself?

"No, madame," replied the curator.

The excursionist looked disappointed. "I don't think he knows," she whispered to me. "It's amazing how they get the jobs. Family influence."

We drove on. The driver pointed to a hill whose top was ravaged with ruins, toast-coloured against the thirsty green. "Les Baux," he shouted.

"I've been here before," said Madame Pinaud, "from another direction."

We got out of the bus and made for the castle. There were a few arty shops selling souvenirs, and a hotel with a view, but the village had side-stepped time. It was a charming nightmare. Richelieu had smashed it, and was still smashing it, threatening the curio shops and the tourist rackets. "Here," said the guide, "is where the world's sweet and dangerous dreams were born." Jeanne des Baux, Laurette de Sade, Phenette de Gautelmi . . . On the other hand there was Raymond de Seillens who killed his wife's lover, Guilhelm de Cabestan, and made her eat his heart. "Where precisely?" asked the excursionist. The guide shrugged his shoulders and waved vaguely. "None of you can understand Les Baux," he said dispassionately, "unless you have stayed here many days and many nights. The nights of Les Baux are like nights nowhere else. I wait for the night." He may or may not have meant it.

I wandered among the ruins. In the distance lay the haze

of the Camargue where I had come from. A gigantic blond man was walking towards me from a great distance. When he got closer I recognised him as the sort of *Wandervogel* who haunts ruins and beauty spots, living on tourists.

"Excuse me," he said, approaching me with a bow, and extending a tin in his hand, "but I have something to interest you . . ."

I declined with thanks and walked away among the ruins. I climbed a parapet and could see a figure scrubbing about in the turf. I could recognise Madame Pinaud. When I got back to the bus, she waved to me and showed me some dubious Roman coins.

"I must tell you the truth," she said, "I got these from a German professor. An excavator. He charged me very little. I think it is important to have a tangible memento of such historic places."

We waited half an hour in the stuffy bus for the Canadian. "The light is too monotonous," he said to me. "It is better in Norway."

We drove to Glanum-les-Antiques near St. Rémy, where the exquisite mausoleum of the Roman Princes stands, topped by the statues of Caius and Lucius, forever caged in a cupola. But the excursionist was eager to get somewhere else.

"We must go to St.-Paul-de-Mausole," she said. "I read about it. It is where Van Gogh died. It's just up the road. Come along."

The Canadian joined us, and we hurried up to a building which turned out to be a kind of hospital. Madame Pinaud plunged straight in, down a corridor and into a kitchen, frightening a group of religious sisters. "She's like a bloodhound," said the Canadian with an embarrassed laugh.

"Can you tell us anything about Van Gogh?" she asked a small, wrinkled sister, speaking with urgent reverence.

142

"Who?" asked the sister, nervously.

"I have come all this way for Van Gogh. I am immensely interested in all to do with Van Gogh. He died here."

"But he didn't die here," murmured the sister.

"Then he cut off his ear, *ma soeur?*"

At that moment a shriek pierced the stone walls, and one of the sisters ran out of the room.

"What was that?" asked the excursionist.

"A poor unfortunate," said the sister. "This is now a hospital for mad ladies. We are the sisters of St. Joseph d'Aubenas. Just outside on the left you will find the pavilion of Van Gogh. Someone will show it to you."

"Come," cried Madame Pinaud, and rushed out of the building again. "I read that many of his paintings are here. Just think. The paintings of Van Gogh. It is worth it to keep the bus waiting."

In no time at all, she was banging on the door of the pavilion. A lady came out, looking like a respectable housekeeper. She listened to enthusings about Van Gogh, and then shook her head rather angrily. "But, madame," she cried, "surely you do not expect the original paintings done in this place. Unless you wish to see some reproductions . . . ?"

Madame Pinaud was thoroughly put out. "It is disgraceful," she said. "It was written down . . . quite clearly . . . the paintings of Van Gogh . . . I suppose you have to tip them heavily . . . it's so much corruption."

We walked back to the bus. I turned my head, and stopped still. There in front of me was a cornfield bleeding with poppies, and behind it a copse of serpentine cypresses, a smudge of blue mountain and a brazen sky. Van Gogh had not only painted this landscape, he had planted the corn and bled the poppies and wept the cypresses. "Look!" I said to the excursionist. Her eyes followed my pointing finger and then

143

dropped quickly back to her handbag, where she was hunting around for something.

"It is written down here somewhere," she said. "It's nothing but false pretences."

The Canadian stood looking at the scene for quite a time, and pulled out his camera. "It would look fine in colour," he said.

THE BEASTS OF MOROCCO

WHEN I was in Morocco I studied Moroccan beasts. They receive rough treatment at the hands of their masters, are overloaded, whacked, overworked, abused, slandered and, perhaps worst of all, snubbed. Very fat men go for long journeys seated on the backs of tiny donkeys, singing out of tune. The same donkeys, in file, patter for miles down long alley-ways carrying enormous loads of sand, tottering edifices of firewood, or cabinet radio-sets; if they bump into people they are hit; if they don't move forward they are hit. No creatures in Morocco have a worse time of it than donkeys except women, but it is known in that country that women have less likelihood of getting into Paradise. They dissemble, and have truck with the Evil One. Yet donkeys, sheep, mules, goats, oxen, cows and horses take their stand beside man in his struggle with destiny. Their eyes are washed clean of envy, anger, remorse or bitterness. They are the eternal younger brothers in faded suits, blamed, patronised and doled out with the smallest helpings. The mules and horses never kick, the bulls never charge, the cows never frown. The donkeys never, in any circumstances, lose a certain winsome expression of acceptance;

145

they are not *thinking* of wanting anything else, like Leisure, or National Health.

I shall not soon forget the woolly sheep I saw in Marrakesh, *following* a man through the crowds of idlers, dancers, card-sharpers and story-tellers in the market place of the Djemaa El Fna. Were I a sheep, I would never have followed such a man anywhere. He was tall, shrouded in a heavy fleecy *djellabah* (surely a bad enough sign), with a hawk nose, steely eyes and the sort of iron-grey beard which proclaimed him an unbending member of a religious brotherhood, one of the descendants of the Prophet. Evidently this docile sheep was off to sacrifice, but the grim *cherif*, whose stark holiness cleared a path for him all the way through the market, never gave a backward glance to the doomed pet. It followed him eagerly, obsequiously, and when it lost sight of him, scented the path of holiness past the snake-charmer, the incense-vendor and the players on flutes and drums. Together they disappeared into a little alley and were swallowed up in wonder.

In the same Djemaa El Fna I saw the only dissipated donkey I have known, personally, in Morocco. It was smoking a cigarette to the sound of a violin (played upside down), and surrounded by a dense crowd of Berber peasants. I met this donkey a number of times, and could see clearly that it knew *everything*. This knowledge didn't make it happy. The eyes of a donkey should never look cynical, they should never resemble those of a barman in a Riviera Hotel. What would happen if this donkey lost its job? How could a soft-bellied, cigarette-smoking cosmopolitan, who has been cheered to the echo, trundle around the Medina with sacks of sand, listening to remarks about its grandmother made by a man not fit to be its dresser?

I think love is the reason for the mood of Moroccan animals. Love deceitful, love fugitive, and love lethal. No hygiene, no

146

protection, no Acts of Parliament, no old ladies with buns. True, the Koran has a kind word for animals, but it is lost in a forest of admonitions. The Moroccans *recognise* animals. In Fez I have heard a villainous-looking boy whisper in a donkey's ear. In the Atlas shepherds play flutes to their sheep and goats while they browse among the poppies and cactus, and drovers, after twisting the tails of their cattle, rest with them on a hill-top, calling them by name. And as a matter of fact there *are* old ladies with buns, and even protection. In Fez there is a *Fondouk*, or rest-house, run by an American charitable organisation for sick donkeys. The idea of giving a donkey a holiday at first amused the people of Fez. They would crowd around the Fondouk and watch the donkeys doing nothing but lounge. It was fantastic. It was progress. But since the drivers could borrow a bronzed and fit donkey while the invalids ate their gruel, the idea soon caught on, and now the Fondouk has a waiting-list.

In the very heart of Fez, too, live a couple of English lady missionaries. They are forbidden to practise their profession, since organisations which attempt religious conversion are strictly illegal, so they visit Moorish ladies in the Medina and help them with their needlework. They are much loved. And much feared. As the donkey-drivers turn the corners of the mazy alley-ways, they look anxiously behind them in case the terrible avenging ladies should appear, like djinns, armed with umbrellas and a flow of scathing Arabic. The first boy to encounter one of them, after having beaten his donkey, imagined that he was meeting the usual elderly lady tourist, floundering in the picturesque, who would eventually be corralled in a curio shop. But no. The lady in bottle green advanced on him, screaming abuse in the vulgar and Koranic tongue, and lashing out with her umbrella.

"Atrocious and ill-begotten son of Darkness," cried this British lady, "miserable progeny of the cursed tribe of the

Evil One, may Allah, whose name be praised, shut the gates of Paradise on you and all your kind." She stood there glaring at him and added, "And admit your donkey." In his amazement the boy forgot about his donkey, which ambled peacefully on for a mile or two, out of the gate of F'touh and into the flowery meadows of the plain, shedding baskets as it went.

Yet perhaps there are exceptions to the docility of Moroccan animals. Once I paid a visit to the half-desert country of the Tafilalet, south of Ksar-es-Souk, and had lunch with the district officer of Rissani and his wife. The district officer had a passion for gazelles, which quiver like birds over the dusty plains of the south, and after lunch his wife showed me the pen where he kept them. There they stood, prancing on thistledown, eyes as soft as duck, nibbling at the breeze.

"Charming," I said, "utterly charming."

"Nothing of the sort," snapped the district officer's wife. "They're brutes."

"But those . . ." I said, pointing at the miniature images of speed and tender grace.

"Those," she said. "I simply don't dare get near them. Particularly that one on the right."

I looked carefully at the one on the right. It was the most adorable of them all, it was made of sugar and spice. "What's wrong with it?" I asked.

"The other day," she replied, "I went up to it, cooing, and it made a peculiar rumbling noise. Like a tiny sort of Métro. Then it charged. I did the only thing I could under the circumstances—I turned my back, and it charged me straight in the bottom. Those little horns can be very *pénibles*, I can assure you."

The other exception to animal charm is the camel. The camel is delightful as a symbol. It carries the treasures of Egypt on its back, it is the signature of timeless caravanserais which wend in and out of our dreams. As I was travelling further and further south in French Morocco, the sight of a camel lumbering over the plain, outlined against a saffron *Ksar*, or sailing into a rising moon, was enough to raise the fountains of my spirit. Eventually I arrived in Goulimine, the village north of Nowhere, in the country of the Blue Men, who travel over leagues of sand from the Sudan and the Congo, to sell strange merchandise, to buy stores, to rest and to wash. I arrived at the time of the camel fair. You couldn't move for camels. The streets were blocked with them. They roared over your neck. Yet when I say "roar" that does not describe the sound at all exactly. It is a mixture of roaring, grumbling, rumbling and gargling. It is an expression of hatred and intense dissatisfaction.

The main concourse or gargle of camels was to be found just beyond the village; an untidy mass of hobbled beasts limping over the ground like testy old gentlemen with gout, showing their hideous teeth at the drivers, who, over and over again, had to tie their muzzles with cord and shout back at them. Intense irritation prevailed. No camel was content to be where he was; he didn't like the camels over there. Directly a driver attempted to move a camel or make it stand up or lie down, the gargle became a strangled scream, and the animal stiffened like an enormous angry fossil. I asked one of the Blue Men, who had been swearing at ten camels for a quarter of an hour, what was going to happen to them all. "They're going to be eaten," he said with satisfaction. A few days later I met the camels again, nearly fifty miles to the north, pitching under an amber moon towards the Anti-Atlas. This time they were ghosts, and the camel-drivers were singing. Weeks later I was probably eating them in Fez, served in *couscous* with raisins, semolina and *sauce piquante*.

At the time of writing, I am having trouble with a swallow in Tangier. It is nesting over my bedroom door which gives on to a terrace. At first, when I opened the door, I used to bump into the swallow as it was flying to its nest. This obviously can't continue. Either the bird will have to wait until I have left the room, or I will have to wait until it reaches its nest. Failing that, I will take the case to court. As this is Tangier, I have only to substantiate whether the bird is Moroccan, Portuguese, Belgian, Italian, Dutch, Spanish or British. And act accordingly.

⎍⎍⎍⎍⎍⎍⎍⎍⎍⎍

GIBRALTAR, HERE I COME

ONE EVENING I was sitting with a friend in an Arab café in Tangier, drinking mint tea with orange flowers. It had been rather a dreadful day. For some reason or other we had made a pact with each other to keep Ramadan. This meant abstaining from all food, drink, smoking or sex from sunrise to sunset. At sunset they fired a cannon and people beat tin cans and tore into the pastry shops and buried their teeth in honey cakes, and spent the rest of the night eating, drinking, smoking and making love. They were encouraged by flutes and pipes which throbbed unearthly consolations from tower and market-place. All were so exalted by the divine tension that it made the faces of the Europeans, by comparison, almost fantastically sombre and bored.

Obviously neither of us had made the grade, and possibly it was our expressions which induced an Arab to approach us and sit at our table. We shared his *kif* pipe, and then he pulled some cylindrical objects from under his djellabah and offered them to us.

"Fine for Ramadan," he said.

"What do we do with these?" I asked him.

"Eat them with tea," he said, bowed and disappeared. I put

one of the objects, which was wrapped in coloured paper, into the back portion of my wallet and fastened the zip.

Two days later my friend Charles and I left for Spain. In Tangier everyone sooner or later acquires an obsession about money. No transaction can be direct, but must pass through four or five money-changers and at least three banks. Nothing is gained, but one feels sly and clever. One's face becomes cunning. Before leaving for Spain I procured a draft on a bank in Gibraltar. This roundabout transaction, which gained me nothing, forced us to take a boat to Algeciras, then a ferry to Gibraltar, then a ferry back to Algeciras.

It was an oddly stormy crossing and we were glad to draw into the Rock, safe as a bank on a Saturday afternoon, sheltered by its neat British cloud. Then we veered to port and entered the harbour of Algeciras. We left our luggage in the *consigna* and took the ferry across to Gibraltar. "It'll be good to get some English beer," said Charles.

As we approached the quayside we could see battleships, flags, and there was a brass band clearing its throat. We climbed down out of the ferry and waved at a taxi which seemed to take us towards the main street. "Beer," cried Charles to the driver.

But at that moment a London policeman appeared and quickly stopped the taxi. It might have been Cumberland Terrace. "Passports, please," he asked. We produced our passports and then another policeman walked over to us and asked us in quiet conversational tones if we had any firearms, knives or explosives. "Or incendiary material of any kind," he added helpfully. Laughingly we denied this.

"Have you any money?"

Charles stated an amount. "I have no money. I have to get a draft on a bank," I said.

"May I see your wallets?" he asked, as though he was politely interested in leather-work.

"Certainly," we said, pleased to encourage his hobby.

He ran his fingers over them and suddenly pointed at mine. "What is this bulge?" he asked.

"That bulge?" I repeated.

"Yes," he said. "Would it be a lighter?"

"It might be a lighter," I said. I could hear my voice going down in a lift, stopping at the floors. "But here," I said, "is my cheque. And here are some photographs of Marrakesh, Tiznit and the Atlas Mountains at sunrise. They are very beautiful."

The policeman was very polite. He looked at my cheque and studied all the photographs. "And now," he repeated, "the bulge. May I see it?"

"Certainly," I said. I pulled open the zip and drew out the cylindrical package.

"Now, what may this be?" asked the policeman.

"A sort of chewing-gum, I think," I said. My voice had reached ground floor and was going down to the basement. I could hear a long sigh from Charles.

"I see," said the policeman. "If you don't mind I will take this chewing-gum into the office. Kindly stay in the taxi."

We sat in the taxi, waiting. "No beer," said Charles. "Incidentally it *might* be an aphrodisiac."

"Would that help?" I asked.

"It might. It would be completely useless in Gibraltar."

We went on waiting. Finally the policeman reappeared and invited me into the office. "Take a seat," he said. "Here is the prosecutor." A large man in a grey suit approached me.

"Are you sure this is chewing-gum?"

The room was filling with the shadow of Dostoevsky. "It might be an aphrodisiac," I murmured hopefully.

"*Might* be," repeated the prosecutor. "Surely that is a very astonishing statement to make?"

"It was given to me in an Arab café in Tangier," I said. "It was Ramadan and people get very excited."

"I am sending it to the public analyst," said the prosecutor. "Meanwhile will you have the goodness to be searched?"

I looked desperately at the window which led into the luminous trivial avenues of freedom and casual seats under trees. I stood up and handed over notebooks, bus tickets, and crumpled sheets of paper containing the beginnings of articles.

"What else have you in your pockets?" asked the prosecutor.

"Loose tobacco," I announced with feeble joviality, pulling out the linings of my pockets and pouring a cascade of dust and cigarette butts on to the floor.

The chief of police bent forward, scrutinizing me. "Is this a constant habit of yours?" he asked.

"Yes," I said.

"Why?"

"I can't seem to find ashtrays," I answered, trying to speak with loud flippancy, but my voice tripped over something, fell, and expired. My face must have looked extraordinarily idiotic, because the prosecutor examined it for a long time without saying anything. Then he left the room.

I sat alone for some time, wondering what was happening to my friend, and then suddenly remembered the notebooks. What had I written in them? Although they mainly contained information about tribal customs in Morocco, I had an appalling suspicion that the customs weren't all tribal. Hadn't I confided to one of the notebooks about the night in Tiznit? The beach at Azadir? The Rawakesh? The things about Lola? Or Zara? Or even Hilda? Pornography and drug-trafficking made an unsavoury combination, and I mentally waved goodbye to my editors, my agent, my publisher, and my landlady. At last three police officers entered the room, and one of them offered me a cigarette. "If you wish to go to the bank," said one of them, "you will have to proceed under escort." I accepted the offer. "Would you prefer the escort to walk slightly behind you or beside you?" he asked tactfully. "Presumably you do not wish to draw attention. The Queen is due to arrive, and there are one hundred and sixty newspaper men in the town looking for copy." I thanked him for this information, and we walked out of the room into the miracle of the ordinary day. Charles was there, waiting, looking pale.

"You are quite free, sir," said one of the officers to him. "You may return to Spain."

"I'll wait for my friend," said Charles, stabbing me with a look of guilty loathing. I could imagine what he thought. Months on the Rock, good staunch old pal, visiting days Fridays, getting the booze for the Release Day party.

We set off for the bank, and I changed my cheque, desperately chatting to the cashier as though he were an intensely respectable magician able to ward off ruin. Then we wandered down the decorated main street, jostling journalists, women in hard felt hats, and red-faced men off golf-courses. It was like Bexhill *en fête*. I had to have a drink. Charles had to have a drink. We mentioned this to the escort, and we walked into a large half-hearted Spanish café. "No beer," said the proprietor. "Tea, coffee, meat-extracts or aerated waters."

We returned to the police station.

"Sit down," said the prosecutor. I sat down. "Now, do you know the Kleinfeld gang?" he asked me, pouncingly.

"No," I said guiltily. My face showed I knew the Kleinfeld gang. The twitch at the corner of my mouth proved I had been with them for years.

"Do you know Carl Eckerman alias Shark O'Mulligan?"

"No," I replied, my life-long association with Shark O'Mulligan, the long years of drug-peddling, written in my eyes.

"What is this about?" he asked, waving one of the wretched notebooks in front of my face.

155

"Notes for articles," I said. "Mostly on religious observances in Southern Morocco. I am a correspondent."

"Are you writing an article on Hilda" he asked.

"No," I said.

"Who is Hilda?"

"A woman," I said.

"And Lola?"

"Also a woman," I said.

The prosecutor gazed at me for a long time. Then he walked away and returned with another official and various policemen. They looked at me. The second official had a strangely reassuring face as though he understood all about Hilda and the religious observances and the Arab café. Or else it really was chewing-gum. The air was suddenly lighter and I began to breathe easily. Liberty lounged outside the door in the half-British sunshine.

"Is this man with Kleinfeld?" asked the prosecutor, "or is he merely an idiot?"

The second official sat down slowly. "An idiot," he said with a laugh, picking up one of the notebooks and looking at it. "Magic in Morocco," he quoted softly, smiling.

"It sounds terrible," I said in a really loud voice, "but it's actually about a conjurer."

The prosecutor sighed and looked down at the floor. One of the policemen started to write in a ledger. It was almost as if they had forgotten about me.

They gave me back my passport and Charles and I walked very delicately towards the Algeciras ferry.

"You shouldn't have slapped that policeman on the back," said Charles.

"You're right," I said.

Every step towards the ferry was part of a perilous game. when we got on board we walked into the salon, sat down and ordered drinks. We talked very fast about the long morning, boasting, ironing out our fright, breathing.

"Obviously the ferry is crammed with informers," said Charles.

"Obviously," I said.

But we couldn't stop talking. The ship started to move. Charles took off his hat and a cylindrical object wrapped in coloured paper fell out of the lining.

THE INVISIBLE PARTY

I STOOD at Victoria Station waiting at platform sixteen, the platform from where I had taken so many travel agency parties abroad to Paris, Montreux, Como, Venice, Naples. Pilgrims, students, masonic lodges, water-colourists, honeymooners, mountaineers, operatic amateurs. "No, madam, you can't travel without a passport . . . I'm afraid you can't take your little dog to Capri . . . The train *does* stop at Newhaven . . . Please declare your currency . . . The sea will be calm . . ." In my pocket were foreign currency, travellers' cheques, and a *carte de circulation* which authorised me to travel second-class from Paris to Modane, and a statement from my travel agent that I was in his employ. I was bound, alone, for Rome, an invalid from an English summer. The curtain had suddenly come down, the frontiers of Kensington, Hampstead and Soho were closed, snow was in the offing, and the wheels of the Grand International Expresses were churning in my blood.

The whistle blew. The new adventure began. London percolated by, fields flashed through the windows, there was a flurry of French, but my heart failed to lift. It had never failed before. The tendrils of excitement, of arrival at Newhaven, passing through the Customs, filing on to the boat, had withered, and the world was prematurely old. Life and reality are mercifully distinct, and I felt I must make the effort to reanimate the marvellous, strike a spark of magic and throw the boring gaoler of existence into the Channel.

As the ship approached Dieppe I slipped under the rope which cordoned off the passengers from the disembarkation point, and stood beside the ship's carpenter and the purser.

"I'm sorry, sir," said the carpenter, "but passengers are not allowed in front of the rope."

"I'm not a passenger," I replied, suddenly inventing a party of a hundred tourists and exhibiting my authorisation.

"Of course, I remember you," said the carpenter. "You're Magic Carpets, aren't you? How many you got this time?"

"A hundred," I said.

The cafés of Dieppe slid into view, the Jockey, the Windsor, the High Life, the Paix, deserted asylums of British bacon and eggs, whisky and water biscuits. I was first down the gang-plank and into the Paris train, followed by my hundred invisible clients. On arrival in Paris I took the bus from St. Lazare to the Gare de Lyon, and, after buying a third-class ticket Modane–Genoa, I hunted for the restaurant car of the Rome Express. Standing beside the steaming, alchemical windows was the chief, checking on seat reservations for the first sitting. Years ago I had made a score of trips with him.

"Hallo," he said, shaking me by the hand. "So you are back to the game. How large is the party this time?"

I couldn't resist it. "A hundred," I said.

"A hundred!" he cried. "But I have had no warning. Who are they?"

"Divinity students," I replied. "They are going to see the Pope."

The chief took off his cap and scratched his head. "They had better come after the third sitting," he said, "though, to tell the truth, I doubt if we have enough food. They are all English?"

"Yes," I answered.

"Then we will give them plenty of haricot beans and mashed potatoes. You yourself may eat as a guest of the Grand European Expresses."

When the bell sounded for the third sitting I took my place in the restaurant car and began to eat. Half-way through the meal, which was being freshened by a bottle of Châteauneuf-du-Pape, I was approached by the chief.

"But the hundred divinity students?" he cried, leaning over the table and waving his arm towards the empty tables.

"They are sick from the Channel crossing," I said.

"All of them?" he shouted.

"Every one of them," I said. "I have implored them to eat, but they refuse. They are green with sickness."

The chief put his hands to his head and walked away. When I had finished the meal I called for the bill and paid it. For one moment I thought of telling him that I was travelling alone, that there was no party, that it was a game, but then decided it was better to leave things as they were. I mentally dismissed the party, ejected them on to the platform of the Gare de Lyon, returned to my carriage and fell asleep. Early in the morning I was woken up by Customs officers opening the compartment door. We were at Modane. After formalities with passports the Italian ticket-collector appeared. I showed him my second-class *carte de circulation* and my third-class ticket to Genoa.

"I will move out of the compartment," I said, "and find myself a seat in the third class."

"Are you not, signor, the English gentleman who is conducting a hundred divinity students to see the Pope?"

"Who told you this?" I asked.

"From Dijon," he replied. "The chief of the *wagon-restau-*

rant, which is switched there, told the stationmaster and he informed Modane. It appears they are sick, so I will not ask you to trouble them." I looked at him in amazement. He seemed very moved. "And, signor, pray stay where you are. You have a great burden on your shoulders."

After a long wait the train moved on. I peered through the windows at mist, mountains and tumbling streams, and told myself I was in Italy. You are in Italy, you are in Italy, you are in Italy, shouted the wheels of the train and the clatter of the bridges. But the fact didn't yet penetrate through the mazed frontiers of the past. A cold city of selves had to be declared before I could return to those lovely lost fountains and find the early compass of my heart.

The train now stopped at each inconsequential station, and the small world of my compartment dissolved and filled with new societies. A Frenchman, folding his *Figaro,* left, and was replaced by a huge Neapolitan woman with a harvest of parcels; an Englishman, knocking out his pipe, faded into the mist. Soon there were only Italians, old men, women, children, suddenly talking, linking their eyes, temporary hearth. I fell asleep. When I woke I could see the lady of the parcels beaming her eyes at me. "It is beautiful," she was saying. "I have heard that this foreign gentleman is conducting two or three hundred sick divinity students to go before the Pope. They fill at least three carriages in the train." There were murmurs of approval, shrugs, smiles. The large Neapolitan lady was evidently devout. She leant forward towards me. "*È bello,*" she said, "it is never too late for miracles."

The train arrived in Turin, and all the people of Italy seemed to be on the platform. Miles of newsprint shouted intimate details from a huge newspaper shrine; those who weren't talking to each other talked to themselves, and everybody looked hungrily at everybody else's wife, child, dog and suitcase. Soon the train was crammed. A priest entered the compartment, and by the time we had left Turin he had heard all about the five hundred consumptive divinity students and was asking me questions. Why were they getting out at Genoa, why wasn't I with them, how were they being accommodated, could he help in any way? The eyes of this priest were clear and fervent like those of a neat Crusader. My Italian was too bungling, and the joke was over the frontier and into the past.

"It is a mistake," I said to the priest. "There are no divinity students."

"None?" he said, dismayed.

"None. I told somebody about them in Paris. Simply as a *scherzo*. I used to conduct parties of English tourists in Italy when I worked for a travel agency. I just invented them."

The priest shook his head. "I don't understand," he said.

"Like Pirandello," said a thin man in the corner seat.

The large lady from Naples angrily rustled her paper bags. "Here is Genoa," she said.

I walked out of the station and looked for an economical hotel. I was directed to the Albergo Centrale, and walked up the seedy stairs to the reception office. "I am sorry," said the patron, "but we are completely full up. You have come at a bad time and will find it difficult to get a room anywhere. There is a congress of foreign divinity students in the city. Apparently they are going to visit the Pope."

I started to descend the stairs. Then I stopped and turned. "Are they in good health?" I asked. The patron stared at me for some time. Then he went into the office, shutting the door.

CHRISTMAS EXPRESS

THE PIAZZA NAVONA was still shivering with the gold mountain music of the Abruzzi bagpipe players. Rome, with ancient opportunistic arms, welcomed Christmas as it had welcomed circuses, the shops bristled with American Christmas trees, Christmas cards and the neat horrible cheer of sprigged merchandise. The season could not let you alone, it nagged at you with rosy imperative children, and a world made up of fathers and uncles. Where could I go? It was not a season for holiday men, for conjurers, hunters of the sun, it was a season for the long savers. "The thing to do," said a friend of mine, "is to travel by the Christmas train back to London." I went to the Stazione Termini and bought my ticket and my reservations.

That evening, Christmas Eve, was my last party before the return to London. I said goodbye to many acquaintances, and in the evening, among a feast of bells, I sought the house of my host. It was next to the office of a registered magician: it seemed apposite that, close behind the commerce, magic should enter this compulsive holy day. I climbed the stairs to tinkling merriment. The old friends were there. It was Paris, London or New York, but behind the façade was the endless,

163

unstilled voice of the Rome I had known by the accident of moonlight, by turning the wrong street—history hidden behind the café, Caesar beyond the bus stop.

There were many cocktails and suddenly it was time to go. Christmas was beginning all over the world, in palaces, houses, huts and tents. The reindeer pattered through the alcohol, and I was led out into the maze of Rome to the station. It was the frontier, it made its own heartaches and celebrations. I entered my carriage and saw it was shared by a woman wearing a fur coat and hat. She smiled a welcome and then looked away. Both my friend and I had had a lot to drink and we talked exuberantly until the train left, then he waved goodbye.

Insulated from life's inexorable continuity, in a wheeled world without roots, I fell asleep and woke up to morning and the woman in the fur hat gazing down at me.

"Happy Christmas," I said thickly.

"Oh," she said. "I was interested to see how you would wake up. I said to myself that you would be the reserved, ashamed Englishman who would perhaps discuss the weather but never refer to last night. Do you remember what you said?"

"Not quite," I said.

"You said life was beautiful. Do you still think so?"

"Yes," I said.

"Good. That is important. It is so difficult to maintain. One has constantly to recreate oneself."

She was Yugoslav and spoke perfect Italian and flawless French. Her home, she confided, was now in Rome. Every Christmas time her family broke up, her son went to Denmark, her husband to Sicily, and herself to Paris. "For the theatres," she said, "to receive the clarity and order of French thought. The Italian language is in the blood, it gets no air, it is made for boasts and song." She ticked off plays in the copy of the *Semaine à Paris* she held on her knee, and then we had Christmas lunch. Sandwiches and cups of coffee from a platform vendor. The sun was shining brilliantly, and I walked along the train, glancing into the compartments where half-curtained feasts were being celebrated. In one sat an old lady, alone, wearing a paper hat and sipping a glass of wine. She stared straight before her and I could see her lips moving.

Further down the train I could hear the sound of musical instruments, and as I got nearer I could distinguish the notes of *Santa Lucia* rolling like glassy waves from the wheeze and clatter of the wheels. In a compartment sat four men: a guitarist, a fiddler, an accordion-player and a trombonist. As I stopped outside the door, the trombonist put down his instrument and clapped a bottle of Chianti to his lips and then passed it to me. "Happy *Natale*," he said, "come and sit down." This was their Christmas holiday, he explained. "We do it every year. We have a job in a Rome theatre, but directly they start putting the decorations up, we pack up and set off, doing the round of the Winter Sports hotels. Come on, boys, back to work." He adjusted his dentures, blew through his trombone, and a gust of *Come piovevu* danced the dust out of the cushions.

I wandered on towards the *wagon-restaurant*. It was only half full of travellers, and a small, unattractive boy with spectacles and a squint was walking up and down from to table to table exhibiting a Mickey Mouse doll. Everybody in the restaurant turned to the boy like weather-vanes, whether from pity, duty or the day's old yearning in the bones, the children, the absent fathers, the escapers and the self-imprisoned. The waiters beamed around the Yule boy, and an elderly gentleman got down on his hands and knees and performed a grotesque dance with the doll. "Christmas is a trap," said a stout man sitting next to me. "And one cannot escape it even on a train. There is a meaning, of course, but it has escaped me. It is simply a complex banquet, and if you don't go to it, the day is cold and empty." He bent down and patted the child on the head. "It has been so ever since my wife died three years ago. The next time I will travel by air . . ."

After drinking a brandy, I walked back to my compartment. And there, suddenly, through the windows was snow; it was leaping up the hills and feathering the trees, it was lying on the land as bright as hope, and the corridors of the train were crowded with young men and women holding skis, their faces glowing with quick gay winter breath. The train stopped, and they flooded out and shouted clear as bells on the edge of the shining early white world.

We reached Bardonecchia and plunged into the Simplon Tunnel. When we came out the sky was grey as cinders and it was pelting with snow. Modane. "France," said the Yugoslav lady. "France." For her the chilly, anonymous frontier-station was already a back-drop at the Comédie Française, the sombre café a prelude to Anouilh. Presiding over the counter was a woman like an old eagle, dripping with courtesy, an adding-machine whirring in her head. "*Bon Noël*," she said; "there's no day like Christmas Day. And with the snow. Monsieur is English? Ah, then how delightful is the old English Christmas! My friends have tell me . . ." The till clanged, the whistle blew, I could feel the old lady's eyes on the back of my head.

"First there is *Tartuffe*," said the Yugoslav lady, "and then . . ."

TRAIN TO COLOGNE

VICTORIA STATION had always meant, ultimately, the Mediterranean, the blueness, the whiteness, the chaos of our strident, civilised mother. Now I was going against the current. This was a Northern train, crammed to the buffers with huge bronzing schoolmasters and ladies who lunched in off-white hotels to the music of Strauss, packs of children as noisy as dogs, with scarcely a dream between them, and lonely red-faced men returning, haunted and nostalgic, to their old battlefields. Suddenly, at Folkestone, England turned right over like a shark and showed the white snapping teeth of its muscular police. Perhaps in July holiday-makers are unduly apathetic; there are too many of them; they have been briefed by their travel agencies, stubbed with excursion coupons and currency; they adhere blindly to their paradise programmes. We stood there (were there a thousand of us, two thousand, a million?), waiting behind the gates which separated us from the Customs houses, the ship, Ostend, Aachen, Zeebrugge, Hamelin, Brussels, Rotterdam. We waited half an hour until the gates opened, then we swarmed in to a terrible field-day of police, shouting, pushing, menacing, a sports-day of new recruits. Were we down-hearted? "That way!" shouted a sergeant. "Can't you see where I'm pointing? Are you all blind? Come on, constable, give them some help." "Certainly," said the enormous constable, seizing arms and pulling people from group to group. "I've taken the number of that policeman," muttered one man in my ear. "I nearly gave him a piece of my mind . . ." "If it hadn't been the first day of my holiday . . ." said a woman in a hard white hat. "We're not on holiday," said a short thin man in a sarcastic Cockney voice. "We're on disembarkation leave."

There were no Customs, and we crammed ourselves on to the ship. I made straight for the bar and went thirstily to the counter. "Get into the queue," shouted the enormous barman. Was he a policeman? He had a slight Belgian accent; but after all the Belgians were beginning to take over, the holiday was only starting. I went to the end of a long queue, sweating, and took stock. Strange not to hear French, an occasional English schoolmaster shouting for Eric or Richard, and a high clatter of German. All the Germans, and there were many, were young, and some of the girls were cool and charming and their voices chimed low like fine clocks. The youths were nearly all good-looking, the noble ones, the sensitive ones, the studious ones, and the rather flat-faced one stamped with the mark of the prankster, the bully in the gymnasium, the one who hates Heine. Backwards and forwards I went in the queue, drinking more than a quart of soapy lager, until suddenly the prettiest girl I have ever seen tripped into the bar, mesmerising in silk, half grotto-nymph, half danger light of the hotel bar, all sex, all sunlight, all shadow, all *Schadenfreude*. She stood there, shimmering, the rare German butterfly, then darted out to her lorelei lair.

"The ship's going to sink," said the large eternal jolly-man in a floppy panama hat.

"Maybe," I said.

He wouldn't mind, it would add to his stock of funny stories. Old Uncle Roger in the Hotel Gute Reise. "Too many people on it," he said. "It's listing already."

"Ha-ha," I said.

I was already packed with alcoholic lather when I met a sturdy fellow-traveller with a square Midland face. "On a visit to my old regimental unit in Belgium," he said. "R.A.O.C. And you?"

"Germany," I said.

We went down to the restaurant, and luckily managed to get inside. Through the portholes was a flat blue sea and a low gold sun, sudden joy, a seagull's-eye view, and we were shown to a table with three attractive German girls glowing in the radiance of evening adventure on the water.

"You'll be all right in Germany, mate," said the Midland man in a loud voice, giving me a jolly wink.

"Looks like it," I said heartily.

"Excuse me, please," said one of the girls in excellent iced-water English, "but would you pass the mustard, pepper and salt?" Written clearly in her eyes were the words *Forbidden to walk on the grass. Kein Eingang. No entrance. Futtern verboten. Forbidden to feed the animals.* The second one smiled sweetly, hesitantly, but her eyes said *Wait for the lights.* "We live in Earl's Court," said the third one. . . .

There we were in Ostend with two trains side by side, both going to Hamburg. I bought a seat reservation from a rather dreamy *contrôleur*, my last chance to talk French, to communicate at a higher level than asking for two sausages and potato salad, what is the time, is it going to rain (but I can learn), and walked up the platform. I couldn't find the carriage and returned to the *contrôleur*. People were beginning to shout at him, but he looked through them; his private dream was immense, impregnable.

"Come along," he said to me. "These people are tiring. You are in a student carriage in this train on the left."

169

"A student carriage," I said.

"Certainly. Here it is." He pointed at a carriage marked with the number 8A.

"In there?"

I climbed in and found myself a seat opposite a spectacled young man in shorts. The carriage was crammed with young men and girls, some of whom I had seen before in the bar.

"You are English?" asked the youth in shorts.

"Yes," I said.

"We are all German. From Berlin." His English was excellent. "There are seventy of us here in these carriages. We have been a fortnight in England."

"What did you do?"

"Intensive learning," said the young man. "My name is Hans. We have seen the British Museum, Windsor Castle, the Tower of London and the Kensington Science Museum."

At that moment a short blond man entered the carriage and made a speech in a harsh, commanding voice.

"What is he saying?" I asked.

"He is telling us by no means to stray to other carriages, to obey the train laws, speak well to the *contrôleurs*, and that he is going to lock us all into our carriages here."

"What, me too?" I said.

"Certainly, then you are a student too," cried Hans with a sudden high laugh. "He is a very strict man, our party leader. But only to the frontier, you understand. Then, at Cologne, we change into a good, *gemütlicher* train to Hamburg. Not like this cattle-truck."

The train started and slid into the Belgian night. Liège, Brussels. I was surrounded by English-speaking students, I was an object for the study-group; the young Berlin eyes were crackling with their high IQ. The exact pronunciation of words, the height of buildings, who was I *precisely?* A writer, I said. Ah, what was the nature of my writing, the motive, the result, the fulfilment? What were my periodicals, newspapers and reviews? What political colour? I answered as best I could, and out came notebooks, address books.

"Will you become my correspondent friend?" asked Hans. "For once a month? From England? Thus I will perfect myself."

"Come," said another less electric, more moody student. "This is perhaps our German fault. We are too serious." He addressed himself to me. "In England I liked very much your casual parks and your humorous sense. I also visited Portsmouth and much admired the air of it. In Berlin we are sharper, perhaps we are also rude."

After the frontier, Hans took photographs out of the window. It was a superb camera, and he also possessed an ultra-modern exposure meter. Was he, in fact, an exposure meter himself? A gymnastic, epistemological electronic gauge? How keen could one get? I felt myself sliding into a neat country of high-pressure diagrams.

I left the party at Cologne, exhausted by queues, soapy beer, trains and the intellectual inexhaustiveness of tireless neon brains.

"Goodbye," cried Hans. "I will send you snaps! Will you send jokes?"

⌐⌐⌐⌐⌐⌐⌐⌐⌐⌐

DR. ADENAUER'S SUBURBIA

THERE WAS, at half-past seven in the evening, Hamburg Station. It was the new German world, built to astound and subjugate the wild, unruly traveller from the stations of London, Barcelona or Paris. It gleamed, shone, glowed with imprisoned flowers, barbers' shops, first- and second-class restaurants, confectioners, sausage bars, milk bars, foreign press stationers, travel bureaux, and an Accommodation Department. Everybody was well dressed, slightly bronzed, and spoke in a low assured voice, the women were decidedly handsome, without being too beautiful or unusual (which could happen, say, in Paris) to detract from the clean, organised masterpiece which the railway station constituted. Along I went to the Accommodation Department, and joined a small queue of docile travellers, people whose faces seemed utterly content to become temporary ciphers for a benevolent bureaucracy to docket, pigeon-hole, and convey, by neatly typed instruction (nearest tram, nearest *U-bahn*) to first-class hotel, second-class hotel, pension or lodging.

"English?" said a stern, terribly clean lady. "I will send for the English-speaking officer."

I waited only a moment and another lady appeared. Her

English was impeccable. "What sort of accommodation do you require?"

"Something very cheap," I said, blushing.

"I understand," she said in quite a kind voice.

"A tenement would do," I said.

"We have no tenements in Hamburg," she said in a sterner voice. "I will arrange a lodging for you." She went to the telephone, handed me an instruction card which contained the name and address of the relevant householder, district, relevant tram, price per day. "That will be two marks in advance," she said. "Have a good stay and a good appetite for your dinner."

"Thank you," I said, moved.

Immediately, I went back into the station, had a hair-cut, shampoo and manicure, changed my shirt in an enormous spotless lavatory, and mingled as best I could with the smart, ordered crowd, asking instructions in my terrible German with a low, metropolitan accentuation. However, outside the station people seemed larger and ruder, more like life; it might even have been an extremely clean and more aesthetic sort of Manchester. I couldn't find the tram (I can never find trams) and jumped into a taxi, handing the driver my instruction card. "Ritterstrasse," he shouted, as though he particularly loathed the Ritterstrasse. It proved to be a long ride, and I arrived in a sort of suburb, brand-new, and clean as a pin. "This is the house," cried the taxi-driver, handing me my bag. I rang the flat bell, waited, the front door was unlocked, and there stood Herr Schmidt.

"Good evening, Herr Karsen," he said, well primed. "I hope you have had a good voyage."

"Certainly," I said.

"Then come upstairs."

We went up one flight of stairs, he unlocked the flat door and showed me into a small hall. Everything smelt of soap, detergents and furniture polish. Any fly here would have died of boredom.

"This is your bedroom," said Herr Schmidt. "Will you please pay in advance?"

"Certainly," I said.

Over my bed I saw what must have been a coloured photograph. It was a country scene with snow, fir trees and a small frozen pond. On the pond a female child in a fur-trimmed coat was skating, watched by Father (wearing a homburg), Mother, eldest son and fiancé. They were arm-in-arm, rapt. It was somehow a quick flickering vision of a middle-aged Germany behind the gleaming modern railway station.

"I will go out to eat," I said, when he had given me the keys.

"Good appetite," he cried.

The next morning I took a walk around the Ritterstrasse. It was almost frightening, like a brand-new plan of a tasteful housing estate. And people are living in this plan, exercising their dogs, shaking hands with each other and saying "Happy voyage. Good appetite." There wasn't a single ugly house, not a tasteless curtain out of place, the shops, though all opulent, were discreetly window-dressed, every object, whether a banana, a box of hygienic handkerchiefs, or a fur coat, appeared a thousand times cleaner, to better advantage than bananas, hygienic handkerchiefs or fur coats in any shop in the whole of Oxford Street. There was even a shop filled with the most terrible oil paintings of rustic scenes (somewhat akin to the terrain of my young skater's family) which compelled admiration for the utter cleanness of the paint, and the brand-new *Gemütlichkeit* of the frames. All the houses exuded an aura of intense industry, and somehow, even after only a short walk, I thought of such far-away places as Japan and America, where, behind the good appetites and the wholesome industry, surely exist the core of the skater's scene and those odd quirks of character which are never quite European. Also, for the first time in my life, I began to feel homesick for the awful areas of the London jungle, the terrible crescents of Camden Town, although quite aware that the responsible arbiters of English architectural taste are only dreaming of what the Germans have already, against insuperable odds, accomplished.

Across the road I saw a modish bar. *Elbschloss Bier,* it said, invitingly, and I walked across the pavement to cross the road. Something shot by my ear, and a voice yelled what, in Persia, Tibet, or New Guinea, would at once be recognised as obscenities. It was a cyclist. I was on a cyclists' path. Was there also a children's path, a dogs' path, and a thin meandering track for cats? I crossed the road, and, the cyclists' world dismissed, again entangled myself with a bicycle, a baby on the handlebars, and a man in knee-breeches. Hordes of bicycles came rushing on: it was like the *Tour de France.*

"I'm sorry," I said to the man in knee-breeches. "I have just arrived."

"———," said the cyclist in fluent Hamburger.

"In England we have no ways with bicycles." I really meant "for" and had possibly made the situation worse.

"*Engländer,*" shouted the cyclist, jumping on his machine and adjusting the baby.

"Beautiful baby," I said absurdly, pointing.

"———," cried the Hamburger.

I entered the bar. It was like something in Gerrard's Cross, but infinitely neater. In every German room, anywhere, women's hands have been working themselves to the bone; the very air is more transparent. Behind the bar was the sort of middle-aged club secretary one would have met, say, in the West Country, ex-army, public school, rowing blue, hunting man. I sat down and ordered a Schnapps.

"Certainly," said the rowing blue. "Are you a Dane?"

"No," I said, "I am English."

"English," said the proprietor. "You have a very fine pronunciation."

I drank several more glasses of Donkart, the air became
still more transparent, the furniture gleamed, and my tongue
was loosened. Give me four or five words of any language, a
sufficient dose of alcohol and I can make a speech.

"You have a good pronunciation," said the rowing blue,
"but I don't understand what you are saying."

Presently more bar-flies gathered, and the club proprietor
introduced me. They seemed surprised. Few if any Englishmen are apparently seen in suburban bars. There was a very
good-looking young man from Danzig. (An electrician who
had given himself the day off. To get drunk, he admitted. One
day a week.) Another displaced person from the East Zone
who spoke English, a friend of his with witty owlish eyes, and
a large glum man in a thick suit with a mouth like a rat-trap.
Everybody tried to talk to this man, but he kept his words in
his purse, got up and walked out.

"Typical Hamburger," said the Danziger, imitating the rat-
trap mouth.

"Damn you, I'm a Hamburger," said the rowing blue.

"Looked English," I said. I, too, made a rat-trap mouth.
This got a laugh. "Not all the English," I said. "Say half."

"Say half Hamburg," said the Danziger.

We were on Schnapps rounds, one mark eleven the first,
2.22 the second, 3.33 the third and so on. It depended which
chair you sat in. This was called Theke.

"I escaped from the Eastern Zone," said the man who spoke
English. He was a jolly man, but an angry man, too, like many
of the middle-aged in Germany. They gnaw the hard bone of
memory. (There are two kinds of people here, the young and
the old. They are completely different. Perhaps all the
younger generation of the European countries are growing

more the same, including the English, apart, of course, from "society" individuals, and only the old men mass at the psychological frontiers.) "If I hadn't, I would be serving eleven years' hard. This man here, my friend, got me out."

The conversation suddenly turned to the Queen. "What has the Queen done?" asked the man from the East Zone.

"Done?" I said, surprised.

"Yes. It is in *Die Welt*. They are attacking her. It is disgraceful."

I could see he was really angry about this. "We criticise everything in England," I said.

"But not the Queen," shouted the man from the East Zone. "It is very important that the Queen should be above everything."

"That's *mysticismus*," said the Danziger.

"If you'd said your Eden," cried the Eastern Zoner, "that would be different. Why has not Eden been shut up in Spandau like the Nuremburg men? He has committed a crime against international society."

"That's what half England thought," I said. I could see he didn't believe me. Black is black and white is white.

"You should come into Europe," said the East Zoner. But suddenly he switched the conversation back to Schnapps. It was my round, and we began flirting with the waitress. "There's going to be a marriage here," said the rowing blue, filling the tiny pale glasses and pointing at me.

I sailed out into the street, walked across the pavement and sprawled straight into a bicycle. "I'm sorry," I said, "I have just arrived . . ." The man said nothing. He just stared. He had a rat-trap mouth. He was the man from the *Elbschloss* bar. "In England," I said, "we have no way with bicycles . . ." I moved away quickly, back into the pedestrian department.

⎍⎍⎍⎍⎍⎍⎍⎍⎍⎍⎍

THE PARROT WOMAN

OUTSIDE THE HAGENBECK Zoo in Hamburg you are met by an enormous polar bear. It slaps fathers of families on the back, chucks mothers under the chin and stands in the centre of groups to be photographed. Since the Germans can hardly move down a street without a camera, men are queueing up to ten deep to take a picture, while the children, standing at a safe distance, gaze with a mixture of wonder and horror. Since children deeply like the idea of polar bears wandering about the street, talking to tram-conductors and smoking cigarettes, they probably do not wish to admit to themselves that this particular polar bear has size 11 canvas shoes peeping out from under his white fur.

One buys a zoo guide and is not surprised to find it impeccably efficient. Every cage and enclosure (something like Whipsnade) is numbered, and in no time at all you can find your elephant, baboon or sea-elephant, without having to wander frustratedly up and down past those interminable vague water-fowl that one encounters in the London Zoo. The guide, apart from exhortatives—*"Please don't tease the animals. Keep mirrors in your pockets. Practical jokes bore apes"*—explains the habitats and habits of all the resident

178

animals, and gives an interesting summary of the achievements
of the world-famous Hagenbeck Brothers. There are photographs of Carl Hagenbeck, a pygmy hippopotamus and
Thomas A. Edison, and Kaiser Wilhelm the Second being
greeted by Heinrich and Lorenz Hagenbeck, with a gang of
what appear to be admirals in the background.

Perhaps the loveliest exhibits in this zoo are the rose-
coloured flamingoes performing their one-legged tableaux
vivants in a large shallow pool, and the huge baboon enclosure
which can easily be watched for hours. Here one discovers
how serious, pompous and introspectively dignified animals
can be, with a sharp division between pleasure-loving adults,
brooding on top of their rocks, grudging each nut or banana
acquired by their cousins, always under the ferocious eye of
an enormous dictator baboon with a huge purple bottom. Terrible brooding insecurity on this safe island on the edge of
Hamburg, with only the children tumbling and hunting in
each others' fur (*"Please! They do not search for fleas! They
seek tasty salt morsels,"* cries the guide). It is only one step
to the atom bomb, Billy Graham and Tennessee Williams. . . .
Not far from the baboons is a tiny sketch of a park with a
miniature lake (Number 23) and one gazes with amazement
at enormous reptiles surfacing near lily plants or twisting
their scaly necks round suburban tree-trunks. URWELTIERE,
says a placard. The Lost World. Between a Dinosaur and a
Megatherium may be seen a notice LADIES and right opposite
are, for some reason or another, Burmese ruins.

I went to see the elephants. There were quite a number of
them, old and young, huge and small, fumbling their pads behind a wide trench and being fed with fruit, nuts, cake and
bread. Right in the middle of them was a young official with a
stern face, eyeing each elephant like a sergeant-major on parade. I could even hear him talking to one middle-aged elephant with rather sad eyes. "Now then, pick those feet up and

hold your trunk out straight." I'm not sure, actually, if he said those exact words, but it must have been something like it. Apart from marching about with the very young elephants and stopping them trumpeting, he eyed the public with a sharp, admonishing eye. "Not that," he cried to a small boy handing an elephant a comic newspaper. Finally he became so annoyed with three baby elephants that he formed them up and marched them off to their quarters.

"Ten minutes before time," said an elderly gentleman, looking at his watch.

"You've got to be strict with children," said his wife.

I then went for a drink at one of the many kiosks in the zoo, and felt something nudge my arm. It was a pony. On its back was a placard saying DRESSURSCHULE. The waitress gave it some lumps of sugar, and it trotted off, and I decided to follow it. After turning a few corners, it took me to quite a large building and walked in. I looked up DRESSURSCHULE in the dictionary and found it meant "training school." So in I went too, paying fifty pfennig, and found myself sitting on one of a hundred or so circular benches facing a large circus cage. Military marches played from an amplifier, and then a confident, smartly dressed young man walked into the cage, bowed several times, cracked a whip, and a group of smart young animals walked in. They were in pairs: two lions, two tigers, two polar bears, two straight bears, and two embarrassed dogs. Oddly enough it was only the dogs who were gauche and missed their cues, but I think it was because they both thought they shouldn't be lumped together with the other animals. While the young trainer was still bowing to the audience, the two straight bears jumped off their stands and began to wrestle, bumping into the polar bears and the tigers, and it began to look like pandemonium. But I'm sure it wasn't. It was pure precision, a brilliant exploitation of animal inconsequence. In a second the trainer had everything in order, put all his oddly assorted animals through their paces, kissed a tiger, bowed to music, and the animals trotted out. The dogs, I was glad to see, for their own dignity, left by a special door. Then came a wonderful sea-lion and a collection of very young monkeys, who actually made me laugh till I cried. Their turns were conducted with the jerky rapidity of an early silent film; each one of them was a tiny young Chaplin.

I went out, and was lured by those screams, maniacal laughter and wolf-whistles which are the special lunatic signature of every zoo in the world, the voices of macaws and parrots. I soon found a long avenue lined by perches, and on these postured a magnificent collection of these deadpan comedians, dressed in smart white, crimson and blue. Walking up and down the avenue of birds was one of those plump elderly women with iron-grey hair who may be seen in any zoo cooing at leopards, kissing snakes, or whispering to ostriches. Parrots were her obvious *raison d'être*, she was cradling them like babies, kissing them, talking in some sort of parrot German dialect to which the birds listened attentively. She was followed everywhere by a small crowd, and all of us, I am certain, who watched the performance, envied this shapeless, grey woman, and secretly would trade any quality we possessed for her power over the Hagenbeck parrots.

After she passed down the avenue, I decided to try my hand, and chose a particular mild sort of parrot with a wise, gentle eye. I put out my wrist, it climbed on it, gave me a cynical look, and bit me hard on the finger. Then it began screaming, jumped on my shoulder and made some sort of scrambled speech. This brought the iron-grey parrot matron running back up the avenue. She gave me a hard look, picked up the parrot and put it back on the perch. She said something to me, but I couldn't understand, she was speaking too fast.

"I am English," I said.

"It is dangerous," she said, speaking slowly to me as though

I were a parrot. She pointed at my finger which was beginning to bleed furiously. "It is bad to be bitten by a parrot," she said. "You must come to the First Aid Station."

"It isn't important," I said.

"It is important. You may catch a dangerous disease. This would be bad for the zoo. It would cause an international incident. You must come to the First Aid." She flipped back her coat lapel and exhibited a badge. "It is a Zoo badge," she said. "Parrot and small monkey section. I am an official. Come."

She took me by the arm and led me down the avenue, past the dinosaurs and the Burmese ruins, to a building near the penguin enclosure. We went inside and entered some sort of office, and a man with rimless glasses rose from his desk and had a conversation with the parrot matron. "You must fill in a form," said the man with glasses. He spoke in American, a sort of careful Brooklyn. He handed me a sheet of paper. "Nationality, date of birth, mother's maiden name, blood group and so on."

"I can't fill up a form," I said, showing him my finger, "and I don't know my blood group."

"I will dress the finger," he said, pressing a button. A nurse came in. She was quite good-looking and terribly clean; there is nothing so clean as a German woman, the whiteness blinds.

While she dressed my finger, the male official asked me questions.

"Have you ever had psittacosis before?"

"Certainly not," I said.

"Now you can fill up the form," he said, "and then I will give you the address of a psittacosis specialist here in Hamburg. Dr. Weininger. He was attached to the Berlin Zoo. There our responsibility ends."

He rose and showed me the door. There was quite a long queue of people outside. Nearly all of them had a finger or two bound up with handkerchiefs.

THE HAMBURG ORGIES

"I'm GOING to the Reeperbahn tonight," I told my landlord and his wife in the house where I was staying in the Ritter-strasse in Hamburg.

"There's no point in going there," said my landlord.

"None at all," said his wife, polishing the sideboard for the fifth time that morning.

"No one from Hamburg ever goes there," said my landlord.

"They wouldn't dream of it," said his wife. "A waste of time and money, and I don't know what tourists must think of Hamburg if they see that nonsense."

"Precisely," said her husband. "This is a fine, hard-working city."

"You can go to the Zoo," said my landlady, "and to the *Pflanzen und Blumen,* or to the great modern airport or the Kursthaller museum. The view over the Alster is the finest in any city."

"Someone is taking me there," I said. "A young German from one of the shipping companies."

"Then he should know better," said my landlady, again attacking the sideboard.

I met my friend in a bar near the main railway station. His name was Hans, a slender, handsome youth with an air of ambitious industry about him. We had a drink in a café near the station, to the accompaniment of that sort of cosy elderly music which England and Germany share in common. Yet in Germany it is even more strikingly sickly, a kind of musical marzipan utterly at variance with the clean, clear modernism of the new buildings. I remarked on this to Hans. "No, it's not young music, certainly," said Hans. "It's the sort of music for views over the Rhine or moonlight on the Elbe. When we go later to the Reeperbahn I will take you to the Jazz Club for the real new German music." Hans spoke good English and seemed to have a slightly snobbish regard for it. "First I will show you the Alster, the park, the rowing men and the Atlantic Hotel where we can perhaps have a cocktail."

"Certainly," I said.

As we wandered through the city, I was immensely surprised to find it so immaculate, in fact I had had a picture in my mind of a Hamburg-Manchester, a Hamburg-Liverpool, and when we reached the Atlantic Hotel the view over the Alster was quite breathtaking, lushly green, water-mirrored, cool, romantic and yet restrained. We went into the Atlantic. It was my first taste of German opulence, a new streamlined luxury overlaying the heavy pomp of the past which still, somehow, hung in the air, so that one could feel an aura of Kaisers and prima donnas and pleasure-loving generals.

"As a matter of fact," said Hans, "this was practically the only building in the whole area which escaped your bombing. Like the cathedral in Cologne. You English have a great feeling for tradition, and you have always admired this hotel. Many of your great lords stayed here, and even lately the King of Denmark, and Queen Soraya. Very smart. Your precision bombing was excellent, I must say."

After drinking a couple of tomato cocktails (everything else cost at least six or seven marks) we walked back towards the centre of the town, and entered another café-bar. The general atmosphere of this, as of many buildings, cafés and restaurants of the new Germany, suggested a modernistic liner, geared to scientific aspects of economy, reflection of light, saving of labour, and visual harmony. Old Gothic Germany, with Fritz and sausage dogs and monocles, has, externally at any rate, been eliminated by Allied bombs and general consent.

"Now to the Reeperbahn," said Hans. "We will take a taxi. Shall we go to the Jazz Club?"

"Well," I said frankly, "that would be fun, but what about the orgies?"

"Orgies?" said Hans.

"Yes," I said, "surely the orgies of the Reeperbahn are famous all over the world?"

"I am sorry," said Hans, perturbed, "but they are hardly orgies. They stop neatly before that. So far, if you know what I mean. But have you no orgies in England?"

"We have nudes," I said, "but they mustn't move."

"Not move?" said Hans.

"Not an inch," I said.

"How strange," said Hans politely. "Let us go."

The taxi took us to an area of sudden sharp illumination and noise. It was something like Blackpool, only more orderly and somehow more earnest. Practically every building was a cabaret, a nightclub or a miniature theatre. Outside each one were placards, posters, or photographs. We stopped outside one which was plastered with pictures of a naked woman on a horse. She had long golden hair.

"We may as well go in here," said Hans.

"Certainly," I said.

"She is a great English historical figure."

We walked through a long corridor and bought entrance tickets from a fat man dressed as a jockey, then entered a room rather like a tiny circus ring, surrounded by tables. We sat down and ordered beer. In the centre of the ring a bronzed man in a sports shirt cracked a whip, while two young, very refined horses trotted soberly round. It was like Rotten Row on a nice autumn day. We drank beer for about half an hour, and then a drunk man got up from one of the tables and climbed on one of the horses. It was obvious he couldn't ride, he was like a sack of flour. "Let's wait and see if he falls off," said Hans, "and if he doesn't, we'll go." He didn't fall off, so we left.

Our next club was very large, and we were shown to our table by a dignified stooping head-waiter. A film was being shown. As we were half-way through it, I couldn't quite make out the plot, but it appeared to be about a man trying to drink champagne, and being pestered by women who insisted on undressing, getting furious, dressing again and then undressing in a different way. The hero was a man with an enormous false moustache and he went on and on guzzling champagne, and finally, after the fifth undressing, he spread out his arms and collapsed on the table. It was really a very sad film, and was greeted with polite applause. When the lights went up, I could see the club was packed with well-dressed people with earnest expressions; one might have been at the St. James's Theatre. Quite a lot of men with their fiancées and wives, and a group of men discussing politics. Nothing at all furtive, and when the screen was rolled up, a very discreet nude parade was soberly presented in which one was more impressed by wholesomeness and an air of implacable cleanliness than by anything else. It could all have been in *Vogue*.

Our third cabaret was also smart, with a circular floor leading up to a stage, and again I had that feeling of being in a liner of the future, of being dust-proof, fly-proof, deodorised, that one's very libido was wrapped neatly in cellophane. But suddenly, from the three-piece orchestra, economically housed on a tiny abstractionist platform, burst the irrepressible marzipan music, the mock Gothic sob at the heart of things, of ruins and dim far-off wars and love for everything, flooding and bursting the dykes and floating them out to an old dark sea of huge goddesses and grails. Imperceptibly, the music became Japanese, the vague operetta Japan of 1910, there was a humming noise, and the circular floor began to rise above the parapet, the lights dimmed and a Japanese scene presented itself. Two quite charming girls in kimonos, extremely well drilled, performed various stylised postures until one of them, disrobing herself, lay on a couch and was fanned. The humming noise reasserted itself, the floor sank, the lights went up and the orchestra struck up a lively waltz.

"We are fond of machinery in Hamburg," said Hans. "Many people come to this cabaret simply to watch the floor."

"But why Japan?" I said. "Hamburg is so amazingly modern."

"Emotionally, perhaps, we have not caught up with the machinery and so on. Which is just as well, all considered," said Hans.

After a brisk dance, the humming started again, the lights dimmed and the orchestra played a sort of marzipan minuet, followed by a scene of Madame de Pompadour and a maidservant. We stayed another half-hour, both secretly waiting for something voluptuous we had seen on a photograph outside the door, but which never appeared, and went out into the street again.

Old Arizona, Mexican Nights, Paris after Midnight. All earnest, sober, prophylactic, many with machinery. Everybody well-dressed, quiet, disciplined, quietly submitting to head-waiters, commissionaires dressed as cowboys, apaches, or bullfighters. And then suddenly we entered a large bar of misrule and disorder, as though to prove that the Germans do nothing by halves. Nearly everybody was drunk, gloriously and improbably drunk. Here at last was abandon, noise, exuberance, dirt, age without dignity, youth without purpose, breaking glass, the disc-like eyes of the obsessed, the fierce cry of the failure, the self-stopped clock of the artist. This was the X-club in Soho with unlimited licensing hours, carrying one far past the waste land into the glorious world of the damned. A strange elderly man with a wig approached me and made some sort of speech which I couldn't understand.

"What did he say?" I asked Hans.

"Some nonsense," said Hans apologetically. "He was trying to tell you that for a long time he was convinced this place was South America, but now he has come to the conclusion that it is, after all, Hamburg. He is, you understand, completely drunk. Would you like to go?"

"By no means," I said. "It is restful and reminds me of home."

At that moment I saw a man in a homburg hat dancing around the floor with an elderly woman with red hair. I caught his eye, and to my amazement recognised my landlord.

He left his partner and wavered over towards me. "Listen, Herr Engländer," he said earnestly, "not a word about this at home."

"Certainly not," I said.

"The home is sacred."

"Certainly," I said.

"To err is human," he said.

"Of course it is," I said.

"Let's go," said Hans to me. "This is simply not serious. It is bad for the morale."

"Very well," I said.

"No one from Hamburg ever comes here," said Hans to me outside, waving for a taxi.

CAUGHT ON THE HOOK

THERE ARE places just at the end of the world which hardly exist, which serve as a sort of gate to open as quickly as possible to get somewhere else, such as Folkestone, Gibraltar and the Hook of Holland. The Hook is quite a frantic piece of limbo, miles away from anywhere, hideously expensive, petering out, among ugly marine buildings selling fried potatoes, into windy sands and a huge grey sea like an angry old widow. There is a small angular town near the port, and you have to walk miles to the beach. The air, however, is healthy and one can concentrate on breathing. I tried to put up in a guest-house near the beach. One approaches through dwarf fir-trees, crammed with shivering children, and suddenly among all this frigid sand and hopeless brick there is a huge garden swarming with flowers. I tried to get a room, but it was full up for months.

I walked back into the town and went to the Hotel Excelsior. It was a huge gloomy building with a smell of 1910, very expensive, and full of old English ladies jammed up against the front windows peering at the sky.

"How long do you intend to stay?" asked the manager, taking my passport.

"I don't know," I said, "it depends on the weather. I'm going to Harwich, but I thought I'd have a bit of sea and sun for a few days."

"Like lots of them here," said the manager, nodding towards the old ladies. "Some of them have been here for months. Packing and unpacking. Great strain on the staff."

I put on a pair of *Lederhosen* and walked down to the beach. There was a gale blowing and a certain amount of hail. A number of quite blue children were actually swimming and in the deserted cafés a few engine-drivers, assistant pursers and *wagons-lits* men drank beer and listened to the juke boxes.

I had dinner and went to bed. Early in the morning I was woken up by a bugle and a voice shouting "By the right quick —march!" I looked out of the window and saw a British Army depot. I lay for hours on my bed listening to marching boots and the barks of N.C.O.s. Should I take the boat now? Why was I here? For something to happen. Something Dutch. It was essential for my trade. Once back in England I might be trapped in the clubs for years, plotting to escape. I got up and, although it was raining, put on my *Lederhosen* and went downstairs for breakfast. The old ladies were still at the windows and the hotel lounge was full of Englishmen visiting the battlefields. There were a few Dutch there too, but they all looked so hideous you could put the lot in Hastings on a rainy Sunday.

After breakfast I went to the bar. It was pouring torrents, and I saw one of the old ladies crying.

"Gin," I said.

"Have this with me," said a voice behind me.

I turned around and saw a small man with a bald head. "Thanks," I said.

"Here long?" he asked.

"I don't know," I said, "it depends."

"Fun, eh?" he said.

"Fun," I said. "Are you trying to be sarcastic?"

"Not a bit of it," he said.

"You staying long?" I asked.

"Backwards and forwards," he said. "I look after the toilets on the boat."

"What's it like?"

"Smashing tips," said the small man. "My name's Bert. There's a dance tonight at the *palais de danse*. Ship dance. Girls and all that. Care to come?"

"Thanks very much," I said. Something might happen after all.

The dance-hall was like any dance-hall in South London. There was a small bar with flags on it where the people were drinking tax-free beer. I could see men in all kinds of uniforms —Dutch railways, international sleeping cars, stationmasters, high-ranking porters, assistant pursers and a sprinkling of browned-off troops, English and Dutch, both terribly similar.

"Ship men take precedence here," said Bert. "You can always get a girl if you are a ship man. The come engine-drivers, *wagons-lits* men, then soldiers, ticket-collectors and the rest."

"What about me?" I asked.

"Are you railways?" he asked.

"No, I'm a writer," I said.

"A writer," said Bert, "that's a puzzler. *Wagon-lits*, I should say at a rough guess."

During the dance I met a pretty Dutchwoman called Gerda. The old buried song trembled in my nerves. I could never have believed it could happen on the Hook. I took her outside and it had already stopped raining.

"Are you ships?" she asked.

"No," I said, "I'm a writer. From London. I'm going back tomorrow."

Suddenly she burst out crying and I held her by the arm. "I can't bear the Hook any longer. I'm coming too."

"That's nice," I said.

I met her on the boat the next morning. It was suddenly a beautiful day and we sat on deck-chairs watching the gleaming sea. "I've never been to England before," she said. "I've got a husband in Harwich. We've been married ten years. He's a third engineer on this run. He's the most wonderful man in the world."

"Oh," I said.

I left Gerda at Harwich and took the train to London. That very evening I was back in the clubs, up to my ears in scandal and chemical wine. It's as tough as climbing Everest, but there are no views.

"Where have you been?" asked one of my false friends.

"The Hook of Holland," I said.

"What's it like?" he asked.

"Absolutely fascinating," I said.

"Did you say the Hook?" asked a man in a marine peaked cap. "I know the Hook inside out. It's awful. I'm a third engineer on the Dutch run." We had a few drinks together. "Got one wife in Harwich and another on the Hook," he confided. "Been going on ten years. Neither of them know anything about it. I see to that. I'm off to Harwich now. We'll have one more before I go."

A PRESENT FROM STRASBOURG

THE TRAIN from Calais was plastered with names. STRASBOURG
– BASEL – INNSBRUCK – SALZBURG – VIENNA – BUDAPEST – BUCHA-
REST. Standing on the platform and looking at the placards
made you feel adventurous and cozy at the same time.

"You stay in the same carriage all the way," said the controller in a fatherly way, one eye on my wallet.

"All the way?" I repeated incredulously. No traveller in
the true sense of the word ever believes a railway official; it
is unprofessional, as bad as not bargaining with a carpet-seller,
or always taking "No" for an answer.

"All the way," said the controller, staring with both eyes
at the wallet.

"I don't change," I cried, extracting a hundred francs.

"You don't change anywhere," said the controller.

He left me and farther down the platform I could hear him
arguing with other suspicious travellers, a hundred francs a
time. I stood outside my carriage and still stared at the placard,
thinking how timeless the Great European Expresses are. The
whistle blew.

I had a meal in the dining-car and returned to my carriage.
It was crammed with French people. They were reading *Paris-*

Match and *Paris-Soir* and *Figaro*. I fell asleep and woke up into night. All the French people had gone, and the stage was taken up by one elderly man with an enormous ginger moustache. In the rack above his head was a huge wooden box. An undertaker? A William le Queux Nihilist? A florist? Did the box contain a bomb, a body or begonias? However, he looked a sober, careful man, methodically smoking a curved pipe, each puff a signal of even thought. We nodded to each other. Somehow I was glad to see him, to fix my thoughts on him. After all, I thought, examining his beautiful moustache, I was a European.

"Where are we?" I asked in French. He took out his pipe and shook his head. I tried my lumbering German. "Are we in France, Switzerland, Austria, Hungary or Rumania?" I asked.

"We are still in France," he said. "Shortly we will be in Strasbourg."

"Do you belong to Strasbourg?" I asked.

"No," he said. "I live in Douai. I am going to the Strasbourg Fair."

"But you are German?"

"Yes. But that is another thing. It is in the past. Now I breed small animals for the Strasbourg Fair. The Strasbourg Fair is a wonderful thing, it must be seen to be believed. Particularly the section of the small animals." He smiled and nodded. "*Kaninchen,*" he explained. I didn't know the word. White rats, ferrets, polecats, otters, dormice, guinea pigs? Or some new, strange, perhaps predatory beast? I felt a fraction disturbed. "*Kaninchen,*" he repeated, spreading out his hands, and then extracted a lettuce from one pocket and a carrot from the other. He nibbled the carrot in a strange, dainty way, his huge, beautiful moustache overlapping the carrot, his eyes on mine, then minced at the lettuce. It was reminiscent. I brought down my bag, opened it and took out my dictionary. *Kanin-*

194

chen. Rabbits. "Yes, yes," I said, seizing a lettuce leaf and nibbling it too. "Exactly," he cried. He was so pleased that he brought down the shiny, ancient box and opened it and out sprang the rabbits like the rites of spring. They were black and white, ivory and fawn, mottled and blurred like fine old blotting paper. "Fifty thousand francs apiece," said the German. We fed them with lettuce and carrots and half an old sandwich, and then they were packed up in the box, the rabbit fancier knocked out his pipe, the train slowed down and it was Strasbourg. "Good luck with the rabbits," I said, shaking him by the hand.

I slept again, a muddle of bells and whistles and interior conversations pulling me back to the London I had left. Suddenly I was woken up. A stream of gleaming officials stood in the bright rude light.

"Where am I?" I asked in Spanish.

"Switzerland," said an official. "Have you anything to declare?"

"Nothing," I said.

"No cigarettes, machinery or silk?"

"No," I said.

"Is that your bag? May we open it?"

"Yes," I said.

They opened it and somebody whistled. "*Kaninchen,*" he said. "A really first-class *Kaninchen.* So dutiable, Herr Kapitan?"

"Dutiable," agreed the captain.

I jumped up and stared at the *Kaninchen.* It was pure white with pink eyes, and its nose trembled like a tuning-fork. "It's not my *Kaninchen,*" I cried. "It's for the Strasbourg Fair." I explained my story. "I opened the bag to look up the word," I said, "and it must have jumped into the bag under my shirt."

"You have a British passport?"

"Yes," I said.

"Then it is in order," said the captain. In the Grand European Expresses, if nowhere else, the Englishman is a gentleman, a club man, above reproach.

"Thank you," I said. He gave me a sheet of paper and signed it.

Hours later, the lights were on again. A tall man in a green suit and a rather gay conical hat came in the carriage and bowed. The hat made me think somehow of castles and quadrilles.

"Good morning," he said. "Welcome to Austria. Have you anything to declare?"

"A rabbit," I replied, and handed him the sheet of paper. He glanced at it, returned it to me, and bowed again.

"I hope both of you enjoy your stay in Austria," he said.

"Thank you," I said. I felt I would like Austria.

In the afternoon, after gliding past a cold poem of mountains, I arrived in Salzburg. I felt terribly tired. Salzburg looked as deserted as a town hall on Sunday. I found myself a *gasthaus* quite near the station.

"I have a *Kaninchen*," I told the proprietor's wife, opening my bag.

"It is a fine *Kaninchen*," she said admiringly.

"It would make a fine pet," I said. "I present it to you."

She took the rabbit away, and I went upstairs and had a wash and a shave and a sleep and then went down to the dining-room. It was very warm, full of bottles and beer mugs and strange wooden clocks and racks of newspapers, and there were masses of people, old men and young men and women and children and dogs. The men bowed and shook hands and played cards.

"Here is your dinner," said the proprietor's wife, "and may God grant you a fine appetite!"

She placed a steaming dish on the table, rich and brown

as a ploughed field. I started to eat, and then put down the fork. The taste was familiar.

"Please," I said to the lady, "what is this dish called?"

She seemed surprised. "But it is rabbit pie," she said.

"I see," I said.

"Does it taste good?"

"Excellent," I said.

"Then eat with a fine appetite," she said, smoothing her apron. But I ate slowly, and the picture of the huge beautiful moustache enveloping the carrot wouldn't leave my mind.

PART THREE

⊓⊔⊓⊔⊓⊔⊓⊔⊓⊔⊓⊔

THE MUSIC OF MOROCCO

WE WERE in the holy city of Fez, just past the gate of Boujeloud, at the beginning of the cedar-spiced, tinkling Medina,
veined with alley-ways and glowing with mosques. Mr. Jones
and I sipped mint tea and watched five centuries roll back. A
water-seller, hung with copper cups, rang his bell and cried
down the ages while a cavalcade of shrouded horsemen
cleaved the crowds who sipped at the tiny glittering shops. A
group of women, like a flight of grey moths, hurried by from
secrecy to secrecy, and beggars sang for alms in the caves of
their blindness. We were staying in a neat, clean Jewish hotel
called the Cosmos up in the New Town. Mr. Jones had retired
from clock-making and now intended to devote the rest of his
life to conjuring.

"So here we are," said Mr. Jones, polishing his spectacles,
"and it's like being in the Bible. But give me the market-places
every time. You can pick up a trick or two there. That's the
thing about conjuring. It's a universal language whether you're
with Hottentots or Negroes or Eskimos. You writers are
conjurers too, but your symbols are too damned complicated.
Don't you envy me?" "As a matter of fact I do," I said. I always wish I played the guitar, sang, juggled or drew light-

ning sketches. "But you must have worked hard enough on your universal language?" Jones smiled complacently. "Ever since I was six," he said. "Even then I hated clocks. You've no idea how much I've hated clocks for fifty-odd years. They've made me look different from what I am. Dried up, trying to burst out of myself. But that's another matter. Yes, I started on the usual kid's stuff of course. Imitation ink-drops, jumping crockery, and buttonholes which squirted at you. As I grew older I bought books on the subject and practised sleight-of-hand with coins. Then cards. Then handkerchiefs and so on. When I was a mere lad of sixteen I could have held my own on the halls. But it was not to be." He looked gloomily into his mint tea. "Clocks. Clocks. Clocks. For all those wasted years. As a matter of fact I did very well. Ask about Jones in Bolton and they will tell you. But once an artist always an artist, eh, and it was in my blood. It only had an outlet every Saturday at the Rotary Club or the Clockmakers' Temperance Society Guild. Not that I am a teetotaller—I used to perform at the Queen's Arms every alternate Friday night until I married. . . . And here I am, a real conjurer for the first time in my life." I looked hard at Mr. Jones and thought how utterly unlike a conjurer he looked; he hadn't the stigma of adventure, a single veil of mystery to hide his square, precise face and Midlands jaw. "Well, I'm off to the market-place. There's bound to be one somewhere round here. Crowds, confidence tricks, spot-the-lady, they're all the same all over the world. Come on."

We set off for the Boujeloud gate, got lost, and eventually found ourselves on a bit of waste land swarming with Arabs in djellabahs and fezzes. They were surrounding entertainers, tumblers, fortune-tellers, story-tellers and holy men selling bits of the Koran sewn up in leather to cure warts, heartburn and loss of virility. A remarkable Berber orchestra of drums, cymbals, and sweet-toned bells punctuated a harsh Saharan chant, led by a black-faced singer who preached the menacing message.

An enormous change had come over Jones. He threaded about the fairground explaining confidence tricks, how stooges were placed, betting techniques and run-away men. "Just the same as Bolton fairground on Bank Holiday," he said excitedly. We stopped to watch a comedian and immediately became, ourselves, the centre of attention. With insolent, ragged politeness the Berber approached us, making a low bow, and invited us to enter the arena. "Go on," I said to Jones. "Here's your first foreign audience." "Very well," he replied briskly. "You can take round the hat." He strode into the centre of the ring, a figure of astonishing assurance, and bowed genially in all directions. It was, I could sense, the well-rehearsed face for the Clockmakers' Temperance Society Guild, good clean fun and a wink for the ladies. He held out his arms, waved them, and produced a billiard-ball, then two, then three, and then four. He threw them into the air and they changed into a bunch of paper flowers. There was an immediate ovation, and nearly everybody began laughing at the comedian. I went around with the Berber's tin basin and collected twenty francs, six buttons and a used bus ticket. Jones, however, was delighted. "You see," he said. "Complete communication. You may be clever, Carson, but could *you* do that?"

We returned to the hotel in the New Town where we were living. It was clean, neat and Jewish. The proprietor was a minute man who constantly wore an enormous hat, and who hated the Arabs to such an extent that he referred to the entire intricate treasure-house of old Fez as the "native quarter." "What, mixing with the natives again?" he would shout, waving his hand towards passing Arab scholars, saints, lawyers, beggars and martyrs. But the hotel was pleasant and possessed a café-bar where Mr. Jones could practise what he called his "four-ale stuff." This consisted of tricks he had mostly purchased in the shady quarters of Marseilles, dubious packs of cards, a Rabelaisian variation of spot-the-lady, and various ingenious quirks to relax the drinking businessman. Also there was a pleasant domestic staff of Berber girls, one of whom was called Habiba. She looked after us in the annexe of our hotel.

Habiba was about twenty-five, with a golden smile radiating from her heart and several gold teeth (of which all Arabs and Berbers are inordinately proud). By day she wore hectically vivid clothes, a walking bundle of orange, crimson, vermilion, turquoise and emerald. At night she became utterly mysterious like all the good women of Fez, and minced through the hotel in a djellabah, veiled up to her pretty eyes. But even then happiness and mischief bubbled up inside her, and she used to hang about at the door of the hotel, giggling at me. Since I never knew who she was, I never knew how to behave. A tourist pamphlet I had received in Rabat warned me: "Grave consequences may ensue if the foreigner attempts to become familiar with veiled ladies!" However, Habiba always gave herself away in the end and all was well. From the very first day we arrived in Fez she had been fascinated by Mr. Jones. Jones and I shared the same room, and in the morning she used to bounce in, in her rainbow livery, and sit on one of our beds, staring at him.

"Why have you all those objects all over the place?" she asked him in French. "Because I am a conjurer," he replied, with an atrocious accent he had attempted to perfect by means of a gramophone. "What is that?" she asked. "A sort of magician," he said. "But you haven't got the evil face of a magician," said Habiba. "Magicians needn't have evil faces," said Mr. Jones patiently. Habiba stared at him unbelievingly. "I don't think you are a magician. You are too white to be a magician. Somewhere you have a house?" Mr. Jones raised his eyebrows. "What has a house got to do with it?" "Magicians do not have houses," said Habiba authoritatively. Then she left our room and went next door, causing screams of laughter and crashing furniture. All the other Berber maids came running along, followed by the fat supervisor, and everyone was shouting and explaining and enjoying themselves. Habiba was a hard, uncomplaining worker, but she went hand in hand with anarchy.

Two nights later Mr. Jones was giving a four-ale performance in the hotel café-bar. It was a great success. He had started conventionally enough, and then the cunning cosy look of the Queen's Arms had slipped into his face, and out came the Marseilles collection. It was an easy triumph. In England, although the people possess a basic honest bawdiness, you have to be careful with the mad Puritan streak. Here there was no resistance. The tiny patron, who had had a stuffed rabbit removed from his enormous hat, was so overjoyed with the performance that he hired Jones there and then as resident magician and reduced our rent. "You see what I mean about communication," said Jones. "It's all so fundamentally simple."

I, in my turn, started to learn Arabic and had short lessons from Habiba. In a few days I could say "Good morning," "Good evening," "Thank you," "Goodbye," and "How are you?" This seemed as good as any way to begin learning the language. The other alternative was to study Koranic Arabic by means of learning the written alphabet and a series of classical Arabic words which hardly anybody used in Morocco. And this method took at least ten years. The only constructive result would be one's ability to read the soft-drink advertisements. As it was, I made quite a bit of progress, and was delighted to carry on an elementary conversation with Habiba in Arabic whenever Mr. Jones was in the room. "You see," I said, "there *are* other means of communication than drawing flags out of people's ears. Quite apart from other obvious ones." "Ah yes," said Mr. Jones, "that may be the case. But wait till Habiba sees some of my tricks."

The next day I heard a scream, followed by running foot-steps. Habiba was racing across the courtyard of the annexe, followed by Mr. Jones. "Stop! Stop!" he cried in his appalling French. "Everything is all right." She had been cornered by the steps leading up to the main part of the hotel. "Leave me alone," she cried, waving her arms. I walked over to them and stood by, undecided. It was frankly the last thing I had ex-pected of Mr. Jones, but anything can happen in this climate and this altitude. "What's wrong?" I asked weakly. The pa-tron also arrived with his wife, his wife's brother, two chil-dren, three guests (among whom was a policeman) and all the waiters. "What's happening?" the patron asked me, squash-ing his managerial hat down over his ears. "I don't know," I replied. "He swallowed three eggs," cried Habiba, pointing at Mr. Jones accusingly. "I saw him do it when I came to make up the beds. He made the most awful faces, and I asked him if he was ill. He looked for the eggs and eventually he found them." She flung out her arms. "How could *I* have swallowed them?"

One day, in Fez, I was looking over a stack of travel pam-phlets eulogizing the beauty spots of Morocco when I opened a folder devoted to the town of Tiznit. "Ninety-five miles from Agadir, on the imperial southern route, Tiznit raises its rosy ramparts in a near-Saharan landscape. The name of this town is the name of a woman. Tiznit herself was the favourite of a pasha of the town. She exploited her privileged position by bettering the condition of the Christian slaves of that period. The women of Tiznit are justly famed for their truly perfect beauty. Milk-white skin, finely proportioned, with a hieratic allure. They are said to originate from Libya or Caucasia . . . Visit Tiznit," continued the pamphlet, "the *souk* (market), the Blue Source, the streets of the copper-workers, and the dagger-sellers."

Mr. Jones was washing his nylon shirt in the basin. I read the statement to him. "I suppose you're off to Tiznit," he said, rinsing the shirt vigorously, squeezing out the water and fixing it on a hanger. "Well, wouldn't you like to come?" I asked. "I'm married," said Mr. Jones, laying his conjuring tricks out on the bed and polishing the billiard-balls. "Then come for the *souk*, the Blue Source, the streets of the copper-workers and the dagger-sellers?" Mr. Jones sat down on the bed. He was obviously thinking. After a long pause he spoke. "I *am* interested in copper-workers," he said in a rather muf-fled voice, and suddenly grinned, taking twenty years clear off his life. "I'll come," he said. "I certainly admire Beauty." We had to wait another week while he concluded his contract with the hotel, performing conjuring tricks in the café, pro-ducing the flags of all nations from clients' trouser-legs and spotting an extremely improper lady.

Finally we set off, crossed the giant white back of the Atlas and wandered in native buses through the half-desert of the south until we reached Tiznit late one evening. It was as the pamphlet had said. Rose-red ramparts burnt into the saffron sky, and every other turret tapered to a sombre stork. We drove into a square like the parade ground of a palace, de-scended from the bus and went to look for an hotel. When we had arranged accommodation, drunk an apéritif, and Jones had entered relevant details into his diary (time of arrival, temperature, cost of fare and drink), we strolled around the rose-red town and slid down a narrow alley-way into a street fluttering with unveiled women, dressed in the silks of long-forgotten harems. On our left was a small mint-tea house which we entered. We sat down and ordered tea. The counter was piled with apples, oranges, pears, peaches and a huge tray of dried locusts sprinkled with sugar.

"Let us try some locusts," said Jones unexpectedly. We bought some, and crunched the withered crackling flesh without delight. It was like brown paper and peanuts. Then some ladies came in. Three of them were decidedly pretty and moved with grace and quiet antic allure. The fourth was utterly hideous, old, and her eyes burnt like evil coals. She was dressed in faded, hopeless black, the hues of Hell. She stood eyeing us. Both Jones and I felt angry and unflattered. Then one of the charming ladies approached and asked after our health and I returned the courtesy in elementary Arabic, adding some French. She could not speak French, but went off to find someone who could. This turned out to be an equally charming woman in a dazzling yellow Berber costume. "You have been invited to a tea ceremonial," she said politely to us. "By whom?" I asked. "By the lady over there," she replied, nodding her head to the repulsive crone. "Thank you, but we decline," I said. Jones was so frightened of the old woman that he took out his diary and began writing. "If one of the other ladies . . ." I hinted. "It is the custom in Tiznit for the men to be invited," she said, "but you may give us some fruit if you wish." Jones and I got up and handed round apples, oranges and peaches. One of the ladies fancied half a dozen locusts. We sat there munching our fruit and then quite unexpectedly Mr. Jones performed a conjuring trick. He was handing an orange to a lady when it suddenly vanished and reappeared in a mint-tea pot. There were cries of amazement, and everyone crowded around Jones, except for the old black witch, nursing her own withered magic. "Have you got a snake?" one of the girls asked Mr. Jones.

We returned to the hotel and had dinner. Jones's face glowed with self-satisfaction. "Conjuring opens all doors," he said. He drew out the small black expenses book and entered in our purchases. Three oranges, four apples, one peach and a dozen locusts. After dinner we returned to the secret street, now winking with orange lights under a dark satin sky. We entered the mint-tea house and sat down. It contained now an air of drama and secrets. Young men in djellabahs sat around the walls watching and waiting, their eyes hovering like hawks, and the girls whispered in groups. It was an antique theatre. There were flurries of movement and regrouping but we were ignored, out of the play. Then suddenly we were approached by three hellish old witches. They bent over us like stricken trees, their hands creaking over the table, and they talked like breaking bones. Their eyes were the swamps of memory. They talked louder and louder and seemed to grow taller than their shadows until Mr. Jones shouted "Go away!" He was talking to a nightmare, and like nightmares they came closer, desiring us with hate. One of them was obviously cursing Mr. Jones, and then our arms were seized. It was apart from the other secrets in the theatre. We were cut off. But saved. A young lady beckoned to me. Her face was lovely, safe as a harbour. "Come and have tea," she said, and the witches fell away, diminished, subsided to plain old women still nagged by Spring. "Come along," I said to Jones, and we followed the young jingling silken woman through a warren of rosy streets to the house she lived in.

Her room was large and contained a canopied bed. A wisp of smoke curled from an incense-burner and a little distance away a man played on a lute, moaning and mocking a light lament. A small fair boy came in with tea implements. On two walls of the room was the hilarious shock of film posters of Gary Cooper embracing a blonde film star. THE GREAT DIVIDE, said the posters. DYNAMIC, UNFORGETTABLE HEART-SHATTERING. Released by UNITED CREATORS LTD. The man with the lute, whose open black face was a map of campaigns, smiled at us with a dazzle of understanding and compassion. He sang to us, obviously extemporizing, and the young lady shouted with laughter. Her arms and ankles were shackled with golden bracelets and her shoes were embroidered with tiny pearls. She pointed at Mr. Jones accusingly. "Bint?" she asked. She spoke only a few words of French. "Bint means girl," I said to Jones. "She wants to know if you would like a young lady at the tea-party?" Jones shook his head. "I'll stick to conjuring," he said, but without bitterness. He shook the hand of the young lady, gave a smile of youth and left.

Tea was served, and the Schleuh lute-player sang a very sad song but made his lute mock gently. I gave him money and he retired somewhere in the house and the patient boy left too. It was difficult to talk to this girl: great oceans of incoherence lay between our eyes. She spoke eagerly in Arabic, touching my hand for illumination. From her little French and my scanty Arabic I understood a few things. Her name was Ayesha. Had I come here to marry? Many men from the outside came to Tiznit, married and never went away. The odour of the incense teased my nostrils, a veil before new tomorrows. They could receive me, I could be born again in dust and henna, grow into the rosy ramparts. I had no need of Leicester Square. "Where do you come from?" she asked. "England," I said. She shook her head. "Beyond France, over the water." I pointed to Gary Cooper. "Something like that," I said. She became excited. "He comes from Agadir," she cried. "No," I said, "over the water. You leave Morocco by Tangier. Do you know Tangier?" "No," she said. "You leave Morocco, cross the water and go through Spain." I said. I tried to draw a map on the floor. "You and Gary Cooper come from Agadir," she said. "Yes," I said finally, "we come from Agadir."

There was a terrible shout from the street. We both started up. "Help!" cried someone in English. The accent was unmistakably Midland. Ayesha opened the shutters of her windows, and we both leaned out over the narrow canyon of the street.

"Help!" repeated the voice, and then I saw Mr. Jones struggling in the middle of a crowd of at least ten old women, fangs bared, nails at the ready.

"Jones!" I shouted. "Wait a moment." I turned to Ayesha. "Goodbye," I said. Goodbye to dust, henna and rose-red tomorrows. I clattered down the stairs and out into the street. But Jones had already disappeared, the old hideous pack at his heels, and I followed a trail of billiard-balls, playing-cards, flags, and a collapsible bird-cage.

Eventually I found him lying in a doorway, panting. "Are you all right?" I cried. He looked at me for a long time without speaking. Eventually he spoke. " 'The women of Tiznit,' " he said bitterly, " 'are justly famed for their truly perfect beauty. Milk-white skin, finely proportioned, with a hieratic allure.' " He got up painfully and began to limp down the street towards the hotel.

Mr. Jones suddenly told me about the camels. "Thousands of camels," he said excitedly. "There's a Saturday fair at Goulimine. We'll go tomorrow." Mr. Jones spoke with the voice of Scarborough. It was somehow the voice of British duty tearing one away from flutes and abandon. "We can't come all this way without seeing those camels," he pleaded, "and you can take photographs of me doing conjuring tricks in front of them for the *Middlesbrough Argus*." So we went, driving south in a small native bus over a parched, flower-pricked plain. A mile before Goulimine the sky grew dark and suddenly the air flickered with locusts. They were the size of cigars, lost tourists as nimble as swallows. Some of them entered the bus, and the Arabs put them down each other's necks. There was much laughter.

In Goulimine we pulled up at the Rendez-Vous of the Blue Men. Outside the inn chestnut-coloured children were playing an aeroplane game, whirring the locusts around on the end of pieces of cotton. The air was filled with a tiny metallic hum. Dead locusts, already dried in the sun, were being shovelled into sacks, and a few people were eating them. "They only come once every twenty-five years," said the patron of the Rendez-Vous. "A real godsend. Camels? You can't miss them. I'll send a boy out with you. He'll take you to the market-place." We set off, led by a small boy with a shaved head. Another boy joined us, and then another, until finally there were ten boys all whirring locusts. The streets bulged with camels. In the market-place there were about five hundred with hobbled legs dancing a sort of angry polka and belchingly roaring at their drivers. I had never seen Mr. Jones happier. He stood in front of the camels, narrowly missing their yellow teeth, and performed a conjuring trick with an egg. I clicked the camera, and Jones said, " 'Whatever is Jones up to now?' That's what they're going to say." The camels hopped and gurgled, the Blue Men came running, round and round the locusts flew. "Where are the camels going?" I asked a small black boy. "They're going to be eaten," he replied, rubbing his stomach.

We returned to the Rendez-Vous of the Blue Men. It had filled up since we were last there—commercial travellers, Blue Men from the caravan route, soldiers, and a faded, painted courtesan. Behind the counter, the elderly patron was kissing his elderly wife and she was pushing him away and pulling him back. "We love each other," they explained, passing me a glass of wine. There was also a girl there who turned out to be Swedish. "I've driven alone in my car all the way from Casablanca," she told me. "I'm on holiday. I'm a probation officer." She looked attractive but rather prim. "What made you come here?" I asked. "The camels," she said briskly. Mr. Jones performed one or two conjuring tricks at the bar, and we walked out to look at the market. There were stalls selling fruit, cloth, herbs, henna, medicinal roots, jewellery, daggers, locusts, hides, nuts, second-hand shirts and Coca-Cola. There were even lucky charms from the Congo. Jones tried to take a photograph of an old Blue Woman with a noble early face, but she crouched behind a pillar. She said something which was translated for me as "It has never been taken from me." Then a boy came up and said "Dancers? Belly dancers? Desert dancers? Follow me." The Swedish woman raised her eyebrows. "Is it quite for me?" she asked. "However, never mind."

We passed the gurgling camels again and then entered the shadow of mud walls. An old woman tried to sell us a tottering baby gazelle, muzzy for Mother. We went on and reached a narrow door leading into a large sun-crammed courtyard and a sudden dark room laid with carpets. Into this came a stout Arab woman, jingling and laughing. The dancers were arranged. Nine women entered the room, one carrying a small drum, and sat against the wall. Smiles flashed across, cigarettes, nods. The stout woman sat behind the tea implements and comfortably shredded mint. I looked at the women, who were all ages, colours and sizes. They began to flutter, like released butterflies, laughing. One of them tapped the seductive drum. "Quiet, girls," said the fat hostess, pouring out the tea. Then they danced, one after the other.

The dancer, as each began, slipped into her secret self and became an instrument of love. No titivating prelude here: the black and gold of the Saharan dances—performed on the knees, the hand speaking. It was under a great tent of melancholy. The Congo dance was fierce, black, and Mr. Jones rose to his feet. We all clapped. Under persuasion, a young girl teased us with her brown belly in a dance from Marrakesh. "Not correct, really," said the hostess. "We are Arabs. The Berbers have charm, certainly, but no depth." We left the house with great reluctance, as though we were leaving a temple or a beautiful party, and returned to the Rendez-Vous. The faded courtesan was still there. She made a bee-line for the Swedish girl, whose name was Ingrid, as though she had been waiting for her all her life. An Arab was standing by the bar with a porcupine attached to a dog-lead. It was staring up at him. "Lie down," he said. There was also a Frenchman with a box of snakes, and a tourist with an enormous naked-rosy lizard bound up with string. "It's going to be a mascot," he said genially, "on the wind-screen of the car." It had been injected with formalin and was dying by centimetres, scoured out. Mr. Jones was at his conjuring tricks again, and an Arab in a well-cut djellabah strolled over and introduced himself. He was the brother of the fat hostess, and was extremely rude to the faded courtesan. "She's dead," he said, "but she won't lie down." He looked with gentle irony at Mr. Jones, imitating the rigid Northern facial expressions, and then invited us to a party at the dancing-house. "Here is money," he said. "Buy wine for the girls. We, by Mohammedan custom, may not do such a thing. Your friend, the cold magician, is strange and interesting." He made quite a sophisticated pass at Ingrid.

When we arrived at the party, tea was immediately served while the girls were elsewhere secretly drinking wine. Three French N.C.O.s were present talking to the hostess as though she was a favourite, intelligent aunt. "We are all married," explained one of the soldiers, "but we come here regularly for tea and stimulation. If you could speak Arabic you would appreciate the grace and intellectual subtlety of the company of the Blue ladies. It is what is really meant by breeding. Anyone who truly appreciates this can never leave Morocco. He is bound by silver bracelets." He explained that their wives always knew when they had visited the house of Fatima. "They sniff at our coats and cry 'Yes. You smell of the Blue.' " "The Blue?" I asked, mystified. "Yes. They are called Blue Men because their djella' are dyed with blue wood. It comes off on the skin and has a distinctive odour." He clapped his hands. "Come," he cried. "We are among friends. Let us show you a Blue Woman." He spoke to the mock aunt in Arabic, and then saw the expression on Ingrid's face. "Don't worry," he said. "It is gentle gaiety. The Christians have lost it." The hostess left the room and we could hear whispering and giggling and then the youngest of all the girls came in, naked with a glow of blue. She was giggling and holding her arms straight out and shaking with laughter. "Beautiful," said Ingrid. One of the military husbands was talking to the Arabian aunt-hostess about tribes in the valley of the Oades. The young Blue girl began proudly dancing, and the other women came in and sat against the wall watching what absolute youth may do. One of the girls was very black and her left hand was striped and mapped with henna. I examined it. "Fantasies," she explained. She started to tap the drum. From nothing, from a grain of sand, the party expanded, bridging gulfs and filling the room with joy.

In the end they seized Ingrid and stained her with blue, and covered her with a djellabah. Mr. Jones whispered in my ear, "A photograph, please," he said, "to make the folk really think." He handed me the camera and a flash-bulb and began conjuring with an enormous coloured handkerchief and an egg. Finally we all kissed and hugged and the girls came out into the street and waved. People and boys appeared from nowhere and accompanied us back to the Rendez-Vous. The faded courtesan was waiting for Ingrid and lent her jewels and bracelets. "Now come to my party," she said. But the patron's wife stopped embracing her husband behind the counter and walked over to me. "Please take a word of advice." She nodded towards the courtesan. "Zara is quite sweet but don't trust her. She used to be the most beautiful girl in Goulimine. A general courted her. She danced like an angel. But now—she does shady work for the boys . . . the Arabs. You see, I overheard a conversation. She's supposed to lure the Swedish lady to her house for purposes of combined rape. There're about ten of them. She shouldn't go." She shook her head vigorously.

Mr. Jones was at the bar holding a bottle of water upside down. The porcupine was chewing a locust. Then the patron's wife came back to me. "You must understand," she said. "My husband and I are all for tolerance. We've nothing against the boys. You see, it's the lady travelling alone and wearing the Blue. They think she's come to Goulimine for that . . ."

Mr. Jones and I climbed in a bus from Fez into uplands of cedars until suddenly, in the distance, we saw the gaunt glory of the High Atlas, moon-mad mountains topped with snow. As we approached them a hidden hand switched on a sunset; the sky wept saffron, lavender and rose petals; the mountains glowed with violet and amethyst. Then it was switched off; and presently we were in Ksar-es-Souk, our resting-place for the night, impressive but not beautiful, its cumbrous, galleried barrack-buildings the colour of stale blood, with the false allure of a cheap film set.

Now, as the bus stormed the last few miles of road to our destination, there was a sudden halt: a large hole was being dug in the road by three men from the South with very black faces. The French driver jumped out of the bus and swore. A tall Moroccan, in charge of the gang, shrugged his shoulders; they had been told to dig the hole and that was all there was to it. "Who gave this order?" cried the furious driver. "The tall man says it was the Captain," said the ticket-collector. Finally the hole was filled in, and we wound round the oasis into the rose-red little town. When the bus stopped I could hear the cackle of frogs and the watery flute of a bird.

Next afternoon I met the Captain, who was in fact the District Officer; he was having his Sunday apéritif with the Lieutenant and his wife, the schoolteacher and his wife and a visiting colonel. "Come and stay at my house," he said. "But I have a conjurer with me," I demurred. "Splendid!" said the Captain. "He must put on a show for the school-children." So we were installed in the District Officer's house, whose verandah gave on the oasis. "Such a tranquil place," said the Captain's wife. "I always laugh when friends from Casa or Fez come and visit us. They will persist in locking their doors, and some of them even go about with revolvers. So silly." The Captain intervened. "Few people really understand the situation here. All the tribes are warlike, but there is no political situation. They live by *lacaida*, the 'custom.' I don't say it's good custom or bad custom, but my job is to teach them better agricultural methods and help settle their disputes. If you're interested, come and watch me at work." At that moment we heard shrill screams in the distance. I looked at my hostess, who smiled. "It's the children," she said. "They've heard about the conjurer."

In the morning the Captain drove me to "his" valley. "When I first arrived here," he said, "I was struck by the possibilities of this barren valley. Some of the tribes had always believed that it had underground springs; but the authorities would not let me embark on expensive equipment until I had proved the theory with results. So I installed a small pump— and now, look!" Twenty acres of experimental farm flourished, like a garden in the desert, with crops of potatoes, barley, henna and ground-nuts. Orange trees were thriving—the whole farm being protected by a wind-break of pampas grass.

But justice, as well as farming, concerns a District Officer. I was invited by the Captain to attend his tribunal. "I have asked for the interpreter," he said, "so that you can follow it all. There's an interesting fellow coming—a mountain chief who was fighting us in the thirties. He's still chief now." The

Captain's *shouash* (sergeant-major) arrived with the chieftain and two elders of the community. "This is really his tribunal," said the Captain; "I'm just helping."

The first case concerned four young men who had abandoned "duty work." They laughed, even when the chieftain sentenced the leader to a month's prison. (Only the *shouash* looked bored and yawned: he was a mighty man who held the names of all the men of all the tribes in the palm of his brown hand.) The next case was interminable. Two men squatted on the floor and related how the first man's wife had struck the second man's wife because the mother-in-law of the first man had seen the mother-in-law of the second man steal wood from the store of the first man's wife. The mothers-in-law were brought in, and expostulated volubly, pointing skinny fingers right up to the Captain's nose. The *shouash* looked still more bored and rolled his eyes upwards. The Captain gave me a despairing grin. "Mothers-in-law are the plague of the tribes," he said; "they litigate with me for hours." In the end, the second man was awarded two thousand francs as damages, and the mothers-in-law were bundled out: this tribunal was over. "Just a moment," cried the Captain to the chieftain. "Here are the eggs for the sitting hens." He turned to me to explain. "We are trying to improve the stock."

At another tribunal, which I attended later, the main case was that of a man and wife in Jewish dress who pleaded for their right to buy land held by a Mussulman. This Mussulman had pleaded that the land had already been sold to an Israelite abroad. The plaintiffs handed the Captain a deed of sale. "God help us!" cried the Captain. "It's in Hebrew. Why did I ever take on this job?" He went on to explain to me the oddity of the Jewish situation in the town. There were only about two hundred Jews in the Jewish quarter, they never mixed with the Arabs or Berbers; they held the purse-strings of the community; but whereas the Arabs came to the tribunal on the slightest provocation, the Jews tended to keep their troubles to themselves and rarely invoked the aid of the District Officer. The most peculiar thing, however, was that these people were not really Semitic at all: they were Berbers who had been forcibly converted hundreds of years ago.

After that case, whose settlement I failed to grasp, the tribunal had to deal with a pretty Berber wife (she would be about fifteen), a smiling insouciant husband who carried himself like a corsair, and a particularly repulsive mother-in-law. The gay husband was charged with beating his wife and pushing his mother-in-law topsy-turvy over a sack of potatoes. The *shouash* struck his forehead in disgust, glared at the ground, and angrily stamped over to the far side of the room. Finally, since nobody else was interested, both the women showed me their bruises. "Do you wish to divorce?" the Captain asked the husband. He shook his head disdainfully. A brief homily from the Captain followed, after which the husband marched over to the Captain's desk, grinned with superb assurance, and held out his hand. It might have been the end of a pleasant social party. The Captain tried to glare, failed, and shook the offered hand. "You're a bloody scoundrel," he observed mildly.

As there appeared to be no more cases, we strolled down to the spring meadow which formed the yard of the school for girls. The classes were mixed Berber and French, and many of the French children were speaking Berber to each other. Fluttering like butterflies, they formed a circle round the conjuring activities of my friend Mr. Jones.

At Goulimine I said goodbye to Mr. Jones and returned to Drift. Now I could write my book.

Drift has a French quarter, a Spanish quarter and an Arab medina. Complete liberty prevails. There are vice, drugs, cheap alcohol and constant sunshine. I went to a hotel in the

Medina and booked a room which gave on to a terrace where there was a view of milky minarets, blue sea and a distant brush of purple hills. Through the walls of my room I could hear a man monotonously beating his three wives. He was actually in the next house, and was a rich grocer, by the name of Ahmed Abdullah, by the grace of God. Before starting on the first chapter of my book I decided to go for a swim, but was warned not to go beyond the river. "Why?" I asked the proprietor in amazement. "It is in the hands of God," he said, spreading his hands, "but it is wiser not to go." He then looked at me slyly. "Unless it is your deliberate wish," he added.

I walked down the beach, surprisingly full of Arabs playing football, and came to the river. "Why not?" I thought. Beyond, it looked wild and appetising, with rollicking breakers and sand like a child's hair. The river bobbed with excrement, but I waded through it and walked on to the idyllic African strand where the sun glittered on the world like a god. I took off my clothes and ran into the sea. I hadn't been there ten minutes before a naked African appeared on the shore, waved and plunged into the sea after me, took my hands and dragged me on to the beach. He made wild gestures towards the eucalyptus scrub at the back. "No," I cried. "One peseta," he cried, holding up one finger dramatically and pointing backwards to the scrub. "Fifty centimos," he yelled after me, as I ran for the river. . . .

In the centre of the Spanish quarter of Drift is the Old Square, which has three cafés and where all people's lives are run by shoeblacks. The average age is seven. They sleep on tables, steal food, and wear wonderful cast-off clothing— chopped-off G.I. uniforms, gas-capes, firemen's helmets, baseball caps and moth-eaten fur coats. Most of them are rather beautiful, dirty, lithe, and all are wiser than oneself. The first day I sat down at one of the café-tables, one of the shoeblacks threw himself down at my feet and began to polish. "My

name is Ali," he said. "You have come here to write a book."
He wore a malicious grin. "How did you know?" I said.
"Ah," he said. "You refused a man on Passion Beach for fifty
centimos. He is my cousin. You live in the Hotel Delirio next
to the house of Ahmed Abdullah, who marries wife after wife
to cook for him, but they all lie on the floor and smoke kief.
Do you want cigarettes, drugs or boys?" "No," I said. "I have
come here to write." "You are in Drift," he said with a smile.

I went back to the hotel, resharpened my pencil and sat
down at the table. Suddenly I groaned with misery. What
had I got to say? Something profound, no doubt. I walked
out on to the terrace and looked down at the town cascading
in rose and white to the sea. It was beautiful and suffocating.
I went back to the Old Square and ordered a drink. "I am a
painter," said a man next to me; "I have heard about you from
the shoeblacks." He repeated the gossip about Passion Beach
and Ahmed Abdullah and offered me a cigarette. Then he
offered me another. Both were drugged. I sat back in a coma,
and the terrible beauty of Drift seeped into me. Finally I
found myself at a party in a lilac house over the sea, full of
poets and writers and musicians. There were also hunchbacks.
"I am writing a concerto," said my host, who was wearing
a saffron dressing-gown. "Will you have a cigarette or a rather
scented cake?" I took the cake and lay back in a dream. The
moon spun on the water and, oddly enough, I could watch my
book take independent shape. It glowed at the back of my
brain, and I recognised that life was a dream. In the morning
I awoke with a ghastly headache and went to the *hamam* or
Arabian bath. "Hullo," said the proprietor, rubbing his hands.
"So you didn't like Passion Beach? How is Ahmed Abdullah,
by the grace of God?"

I was back in the café in the Old Square, and I resolutely
took out a crumpled sheet of paper from my pocket, wrote
Chapter One and then ordered an anis. Ali came up to me

221

and dived at my shoes. "No," I cried. "I am poor." "Non-sense," he said, busy polishing. "All you in Drift are rich and idle. Why aren't you at the port? The boat is arriving."

"Which boat?" I asked.

"The boat with all the expelled people from the countries over the sea," he said. "Everyone goes down there. Do you want some filthy pictures?"

"No," I said.

"Would you like a whore?"

"No," I said. "I am writing a book."

"I will find you a woman. Nobody lives without something in Drift."

Ramadan arrived with a burst of a cannon, and suddenly all the Arabs looked miserable and scowled at the intellectuals in the cafés. From sunrise to sunset the Arabs couldn't eat or smoke or have sex. "More than we could ever do with all our advanced ideas," said the painter. Then one day the shoe-black beckoned to me mysteriously and I followed him through winding alleyways and we came to a cabaret called La Cucuracha. Here I met, with surprise, a charming, dark girl called Rosita. "Do you like her?" "Very much," I said. "She doesn't need any money," he whispered. Rosita and I held hands, and we looked into each other's eyes. It was as if we had known each other for years, as if we had lived and died together down the centuries. We wandered back to the hotel in the Medina. I tussled with her deliciously for an hour. She was tender, insinuating and as sharp as a diamond. She came from Jerez de la Frontera, and somewhere at the back of my mind was the picture of a witch. After a time I was in a spell. I tried to fight it. It was far worse for Chapter One than Blackpool. I had made a mistake. You cannot write a book any better in a spell than when you are dull or unhappy.

I was sitting at the café when Ali came up to me, grinning. "She's gone," he said. "Who's gone?" I asked. "Rosita. It happens in Drift. She's sitting over at the café opposite." I looked across and saw her sitting with a man dressed in a superb suit. Her eyes were shining. Looking closer, I recognised the man as the one who had accosted me at Passion Beach. "Do you want any drugs?" asked Ali. "No," I said. "I'm writing a book."

One day, going down to have a swim, I met a man called Roger Barnett whom I had once met in the Chaos. "Hallo," he cried, looking very debonair. "What are you doing here in Drift?" "Writing a book," I said. "Splendid," said Barnett. "It's a wonderful life being a writer. Go anywhere you want. No worries. And you couldn't find a better place than Drift. Do as you please. Wonderful climate." "What are you doing, yourself?" I asked. "Oh, I'm a writer too," he said. "Just on the point of getting ready, as it were. Making preparatory notes. All that sort of thing. I live here in an Arab's house, as a matter of fact. Come and have lunch. I'm free for quite a long time, I hope. I'm expecting a telegram."

We had a swim and then went, through winding streets, to his house in the Calle Oued. "It's not far," said Barnett. "First on the left past the Coca-Cola sign." We turned left and passed droves of children playing intricate games and arrived in front of a small house fronted with peeling stucco. Barnett knocked on the door, a small window opened and eyes peered out at us. Barnett said something in Arabic and the door opened. I saw a young girl in a white djellabah, holding a broom. "Berber girl," said Barnett. "You can change them once a week in the market. Come and have a drink." We sat down in the Arab sitting-room on low couches covered with red cushions. "Do you smoke?" asked Barnett. "Smoke?" I said. "Yes. Kief." "Yes," I said. "It helps thought," he said. He clapped his hands and the Fatima or Arab servant appeared and he said something to her in Arabic. She filled two long, beautiful pipes and we took them and she lit them for us. Soon we were floating away.

"I wish I was back in London," said Barnett. "What's the point of going to London?" I said. "Just to be there," said Barnett; "just to look at the old red houses and see Marshall and Snelgroves and see the eight McGregors again." "It seems pointless," I said, "unless you had legitimate business there. Or if you were in love with someone. Or you were inheriting money, or something like that." "I would like to write there. It's a solid place. Here, I am always making preparatory notes," said Barnett. "They come to me in the middle of the night and then I forget them. But I suppose I'll get my telegram soon. Come up and look at the tortoises." "Which tortoises?" "Up on the roof," said Barnett.

We climbed up narrow stairs and up on to a sort of parapet. The sun was absolutely blazing and the sky had a frightening intensity. The floor of the parapet was crawling with tortoises and they were all eating lettuces. "It costs a lot," said Barnett, "but I feel sorry for them." "Where do they come from?" I asked. "They get lost in the streets," he said, "and they roast them in the small Arab cafés. The children bring them to me and I give them sweets. Knowing Arabs, I'm pretty sure they go right out into the country and catch them." "They look cheerful," I said. "If tortoises can look cheerful," said Barnett. "They get covered with horrible ticks. Do you mind de-ticking tortoises? I've got some forceps." "Not a bit," I said. He went down and brought me the forceps and I sat on the parapet, de-ticking tortoise after tortoise. It was hard work, and sometimes the tortoises screamed. But it was satisfactory, positive work. Barnett looked sick. "I don't know how you can do it," he said. "I've done lots of things," I said. Eventually all the tortoises were clean and easy and crunching into their lettuce. "Come and have another smoke," said Barnett, "and some more wine."

In the town of Drift in North Africa most of the smart people live in the French quarter, but the distinguished ones live up in the Kasbah, in tiny, sly cramped houses without any chairs or baths or sanitation. You climb a corkscrew stair to a tower, and gasp at Drift thrown like an exquisite carpet to the floor of the sea. Through fox-eyed windows come the cries of the Arab boys kicking footballs, the eyeless chant of the beggars, the drugged network of Arab music blaring from radios in cunning shops. It is a stone's throw away from cocktail bars, Spanish tarts, mushroom banks, tourists and Drift Radio flamenco, but nothing of Europe comes through the sandalwood barrier. It's as strong as steel, wide as a sea. Here is Ispahan or old fabulous Baghdad or rosy Marrakesh, and Allah rules the fierce brilliant sky. The people who come to live in the Kasbah do not stay the same. Their eyes change colour, their problems change, time is huge, there is importance in tiny things, life and death have dangerous, absorbing double faces.

High up in the Kasbah is the Palace of the Djinns. This is a sort of Arabian nightclub, managed by a man called Ivan West. I had known him years ago in Paris, and he seemed to have no nationality, no profession and no income. At times he seemed American, at times English, at others French. He was intensely vague, and had a habit of suddenly disappearing. On one occasion I heard that he disappeared from the Gare d'Austerlitz in a dressing-gown to go to a wedding in Biarritz. There was no wedding, but he stayed there for months at a very good hotel. He was an unhappy man, but gave the impression of being very close to the smartest and highest points of excitement to be found anywhere.

Hearing that he was running the Palace of the Djinns, I left my crumbling Spanish hotel near the seafront and climbed up the shrill, masked streets of the Kasbah towards the building. It was night, and this is a time when the Kasbah is given over to the magicians. After tunnelling into various sly alley-ways I discovered the Palace, a rather dilapidated house with a huge red door. In front stood a bearded man in a turban, and he bowed me inside. I felt almost struck by the magnificence of the place—a cool, restrained magnificence, half ascetic, half voluptuous, secretively divided into glimmering compartments overhung by Arabian lamps like autumn moons. An orchestra was playing and chanting, and the rhythm tapped and tapped at your mind like a brilliant messenger. I went into the bar and found West. He was standing in front of an elegant chair on which was sitting a kind of small owl which he was feeding with pieces of liver. West was dressed in well-cut evening clothes, and seemed more interested in this owl than in anything he had ever known, as though he had only lived and suffered to find it. But that was just an impression. "Hullo," he said, holding out his hand. We both sat down beside the owl. It had a disturbing habit of swivelling its head round backwards and looking at you with remarkable intensity, like a lawyer, then swaying. "It's a bit drunk," admitted West. "I give it Martinis, you know."

The music kept creeping up on me like a tide, and a small boy in a turban came into the bar, chanting and twirling and stuffing money into his hair. "You have to give him money," said West. "These are Berbers. Like a sect." "The orchestra is quite the most beautiful orchestra I have ever heard," I said. West nodded his head vaguely, absorbed in the bird. By now it was looking at itself in the mirror, crouching and swaying and swivelling. Viewed from the back, you could see its absurd ungrown bottom. "It's a Thurber owl," I cried delightedly. "It's that and more," he agreed, giving it a drink of gin and vermouth. Then, suddenly, and as I remembered from the Paris days, he began telling me a wonderful story. It was about the Palace of Djinns and the orchestra.

226

"I got the musicians from a place in the Riff Mountains," he said. "I have been there once or twice. It is guarded, you know. A valley. These people are not really Mohammedans, they are a strange race who come from old Carthage. All their feasts commemorate the marriage of Ishtar with the great god Pan, and this is the music you are hearing. It is really and actually the pipes of Pan. They live for music, and play by families; and although I change my orchestra once a month the new ones are always relatives." "What is it like in this valley?" I asked excitedly. "It is astonishingly beautiful, rather somnolent," he said. "The drums start almost at dawn, and then the pipes call to each other, and there is this kind of intricate musical rivalry between the families. It is something like living with birds." He turned to the owl. By now it was hunting itself behind the mirror, coming back and shuffling past it, now with cunning, now swivelling towards us with its drunk lawyer's eyes. "They are like children," continued West, "and of course I am betraying them . . . They always need me with them, and I have had to learn the drum ritual. It is a sort of love." He suddenly left the owl and walked towards the orchestra, and I could hear them playing to him, while he moved slightly backwards and forwards in a light trance. There was nothing insincere about him. A sharp brittle drum seemed to call him and a heavy drum pushed him away. Sometimes the orchestra laughed delightedly as they teased him with the music. When he returned to me and the owl he looked very sad and tired. "I am betraying them," he said. "Hardly anybody knows what's going on here. If you really listened to the pipes of Pan, if you *cared* to, you would go mad, and the world would always be empty afterwards." "Who comes here?" I asked him, waving towards the European people in evening dress drinking wine and eating expensive cous-cous. "Film-stars and American generals and people from yachts, and some of them come from Cook's, and smart, bogus intellectuals." He gave the owl a drink. "I am always betraying what I love."

And then he laughed, pointing at the owl. "Do you know," he said, "when this owl grows up it will become terribly terribly fierce and swoop on people and bite them?"

Everyone in Drift, from the international Administration officials down to the tiniest flea, keeps praying for tourists. A thousand bars and cafés stretch out their tentacles to draw them in, from the smart, hard bars in the French quarter where Africa is shut out like a stray cat, and where there are no pattering animals, no flutes, and no whirling dervishes, to the shrill Spanish bars sweating with flamenco. There is also a foundering tea-room called the Arabian Nights, kept by a Miss Fisk, which is situated near the Kasbah.

The Arabian Nights has Arabian décor, a glimpse of the sea from one of the lavatories, and tables covered with the *Illustrated London News*. There is a choice of mint tea or potted tea with milk, and no genuine Arab ever goes near it, except for the Fatima. To be sure the furniture, stools, hangings and carpets are not genuine, but they possess a faint and not entirely depressing tang of the East. Poor Miss Fisk was always having trouble of some kind with her Fatimas. One stole from her, another poisoned her parrot, and a third burnt her letters. "It's enough to send me back to Frinton," she told me, "but I'm going to hang on. The tourists are bound to come again, and one day I'll find a good Fatima."

One day I was sitting at a café in the French quarter, drinking a coffee and worrying about money, when I was approached by one of the tourists. He was a tall, thin parson with the precise face of a man with regular habits. He addressed me in very slow and painful French. "I am English," I said. "What a relief," he said. "Speaking French in this heat gives me indigestion. Or perhaps it is the oil. I wanted some advice, and it struck me that you are a Drift citizen." I did not quite know how to take this, because I had omitted to shave that morning, but I smiled. "I am not a Drift citizen," I said, "but I know the town a little. Particularly the Spanish quarter." "Excellent," said the parson. "My name is Carruthers and I am one of the members of a Protestant Convention which is visiting Drift. As a form of relaxation we are instituting a kind of tea-party tomorrow afternoon—wives and so on—and I particularly need to know a place with the right kind of atmosphere." He looked at me questioningly. "What sort of atmosphere?" I asked. "Something vaguely Arab," he said with a small smile. "But not too Arab, if you know what I mean. With a view. And where we can get real tea. With milk and cakes. You know, kept by someone fairly clean but not too friendly. The people here are inclined to cling." He then told me of his experiences with people trying to sell him lottery tickets, cheese and combs. "I very nearly struck out at a terrible man shoving an octopus in my face," he said. I thought for a while and suddenly remembered the Arabian Nights. It seemed just the place. I told Mr. Carruthers and suggested that I should call on Miss Fisk personally and arrange it for him. "That is very kind of you," he said. "There will be twelve in the party." I made a rapid calculation of the commission, shook hands with Mr. Carruthers, and left for the main square.

The Arabian Nights tea-rooms were on the second floor of a heterogeneous building containing an international marriage bureau and a strange doctor who proclaimed himself an expert on diseases of the bladder, but was never in. I discovered later that he was very ill. I climbed the stairs and opened the door of the tea-rooms. Miss Fisk was sitting on an ottoman and seemed worried. She was a round woman with dust-coloured hair and surprising blue candid eyes. They were the eyes of Bournemouth on a sunny day. "It's my Fatima," she said. "I had to speak to her sharply the other day, and then I found her in the kitchen trying to cast a spell on me, and I gave her notice. She's leaving tomorrow. Oh, Drift, Drift . . ." I told her about Mr. Carruthers and the party, and that it was a special occasion, and would she supply the very best tea and milk and some nice cakes. "I'll tell the Fatima," said Miss Fisk.

When I next met Mr. Carruthers I told him that everything was arranged, and he invited me to the tea-party "for the trouble you've taken and you can talk to us about Drift." Normally, in England, I would never be invited to a Protestant Convention tea-party, but it did not seem too remarkable here. The next day I would have forgotten all about it if I hadn't heard a church bell ringing behind the big square, and I jumped up and peered at the clock. I was half an hour late.

I set off for the tea-rooms and pushed open the door. I was met by Miss Fisk. She stared at me for a long time and then slowly pointed at the ceiling. "What?" I asked. "The ceiling," she repeated. "But what about the ceiling?" I asked. "So high," she murmured, and I looked at her in amazement. I followed her into the main parlour and saw the twelve clients seated in a corner of the room near the bogus copper kettle. One of them was on the floor shredding flowers. Mr. Carruthers was seated on a couch behind a low table, laughing softly to himself. "Mr. Carruthers," I said, "I am sorry I am late." He stopped laughing in that peculiar way and looked at me with terrible intentness. "I can see right through you," he said. "And the wall," he added. Then he began laughing again quite mirthlessly. Three women of the party were playing something that looked like pat-a-cake, patting hands and talking in a random way about Glamorgan. I sat down and suddenly discovered a woman under the table. She was looking at me with the cold, fierce focus of an insect. I looked back at her and she said, "I am Mrs. Corcoran." "Good afternoon," I said. "Never mind about the afternoon," she said, and began eating lettuce. There was something wrong in the atmosphere and memory tugged at my sleeve. Hadn't I been through all this before, a week after arriving in Drift? Those parties in the lilac house by the sea? I approached Miss Fisk, who was dancing slowly and hieratically in the middle of the floor. "Miss Fisk," I asked, "what has been going on?" "On," she repeated. "On. On and on and on and on. It's all been going on. There's nothing to stop it."

Then I knew what had happened. I marched into the kitchen and seized the Fatima by the shoulders. "What have you done?" I asked her. "Nothing," she said, "nothing. Why should I do anything? I am leaving." "What did you do with the cakes?" I asked her. "Nothing," she said. I looked at her insistently. Fatimas can be like snakes, smooth and glistening. "Well," she said, seizing her djellabah, slipping into it and making for the door, "I'm going." I followed her down the stairs and shouted to her from the door. "What was in the cakes?" I cried. "Perhaps hashish," she cried back, waving with sudden gaiety. "Goodbye."

LOOKING FOR CARLOS

WHEN I said I was going to Galicia the neat sun-glassed Catalans roared with laughter. "People don't *go* to Galicia," they said, "they get shipwrecked there." They then told me a lot of dirty jokes, some of which were quite funny. Galicia, it appeared, was a land of enormous libidinous women like cows ("splendid milk"), bagpipes and fog. Scenery they threw in like a gift because I was English, in the same way that they might have said whisky or dogs. "It's very green," they said, "if you like that sort of thing. Plenty of crabs and so on." "But I've got to go to Galicia," I said. "For a book." "Well, of course, if they're sending you there . . ." they said, splitting their sides.

I decided to go to Madrid. Madrid, by now, was the true centre of the world, it was the only paradoxical city left in Europe. "Madrid," cried the Catalans, shaking with laughter. "Nobody goes near Madrid except crooks and lay-abouts and government officials. Rich widows? You are too old for that. The heat at this time of year is atrocious, and the wine sends you mad. Also the people of Madrid have false faces, they fall all over you, they smell out money like fleas in a poor-house, and leave you as thin as a new priest." "Where shall I go?" I asked desperately, my life dominated by wine and print. "Barcelona," they said. "Of course." Days later, gnawed by guilt, I went to the offices of Spanish Railways and bought a ticket to Madrid.

Harry Austen had given me introductions to a man called Carlos, who played the bassoon on the wireless, and an official of the Bank of Spain. I received the two letters and the next morning I crept to the railway station and rattled south. It was a journey like all Spanish journeys. In ten minutes you knew everyone in the compartment intimately, in an hour the whole carriage, in two hours the entire train. When night falls it is a slowly moving population of noise. Sleep is not considered. If you sleep, the devils creep in from the plain and the owls will eat your liver. On this journey I actually heard a snoring soldier discuss the death of someone's aunt with a policeman who was eating black sausage and bread. I was swept by a sudden intolerable sadness, a guilt, a loneliness. There, over the unlit plains, were warrens and shacks and holes of love and tears, and the ghosts chattered in the tiny battered graveyards. Of aunts, and grandfathers, and olive oil and grandsons and saints as solid as bakers.

In the morning there was Madrid. I found a taxi and gave the address of the bassoon-player. His name was Carlos Prieto. "He's a good chap," Austen had said. "Just your sort. Fat and Bohemian and drinks like a fish." I showed the address to the taxi-driver, and he shook his head. "Never heard of it," he said. He drove off in a vague direction for miles and miles and ended up in a sort of pine forest. It reminded me of Tarragona. The driver got out of his taxi and spoke to a policeman. The policeman scratched his head and sent us to the police station. In the police station we studied maps. "These are old maps," apologised the inspector. "Pre-war. They have changed a lot of the street-names since then." A very old policeman remembered that a nephew had been seen shot in a street which bore the same name as the one I was seeking. He pointed at the map and we set off. An hour passed, and the taxi-meter stood at one hundred and twenty pesetas. The taxi-driver spoke to road repairers, whores, children and old black women with a maze of memories. Finally we found a small, sharp boy on a bicycle, delivering lettuce and tomatoes. "There is a Prieto," he said. "He lives three streets away." "Does he play the bassoon?" asked the taxi-driver. "Probably," said the small, sharp boy. "He is an artist." We followed the boy to a derelict house with shuttered windows and an air of damp regret. The gate was hammered in with a nail. "Nobody appears to live here," said the taxi-driver. "Do you deliver here?" "No," said the sharp boy. "Señor Prieto doesn't eat lettuce." At last a woman came to the door of the next-door house and told us that Señor Prieto had moved to another quarter of the town. He played some sort of instrument, she said. She had heard it, she said. Loud, she said. She looked angry. We took the address and drove more and more miles away into a flat landscape with shacks. The meter stood at two hundred pesetas. I banged the front window of the taxi and shouted into the ear of the taxi-driver. "I can't go on like this," I cried. "I'm not an American. I'm a poor English writer." "It's not my fault," shouted the driver. "I don't know every bassoon-player in Madrid who doesn't happen to eat lettuce." It was terribly hot, and the taxi was invaded by flies. I thought desperately of Galicia, bright green and cool, with huge moist milky women and the wind of bagpipes.

"Here," said the taxi-driver, suddenly pulling up. We were in front of a sort of cave. He got out of the taxi and shouted, and out of the cave came hens, and cats and two dogs and a goat and masses of children, and finally a huge man in a dirty white shirt. "Are you Señor Prieto?" asked the taxi-driver. "By the Grace of God I am," replied the huge man, kicking away a hen and a cat. "Do you play the bassoon?" "Certainly

not," said the huge man. "I suffer from ulcers." He waved
at the cave. I got out of the taxi and bowed at him. "I am looking for a certain Señor Prieto who plays the bassoon for the
wireless. Are you a relation?" The huge man in the dirty shirt
suddenly roared with laughter. I might have been on the
moon. "María Asunción," he roared, and a woman came out
of the cave with the thin white face of an Andalusian Virgin.
"Am I a relation of a man who plays the bassoon for the wireless?" he asked her. "Certainly not," replied the woman, crossing herself. "Come into the cave, then," cried the cave-owner.
"Misfortune makes all hearts companions, and a bad tooth
cannot crack nuts. We have olives and a rather sour wine."
"No, thank you," I said, backing into the taxi, and noting
that the meter announced two hundred and fifty pesetas.

"Where now?" asked the taxi-driver in a sort of comic
voice. "The Bank of Spain," I said. I took out the second letter
and re-read it. It was addressed to Antonio Vegas. "Illustrious
and revered friend," it said, "the bearer of this letter is no
other than Anthony Carson, the famous and distinguished
English writer, humorist and student of Spanish institu-
tions . . ." After an hour's travel, I found myself among familiar trains, parks and smart cafés. Leaning out of the window, I saw the sort of women who only breathe in Madrid.
They are like sparks, caught between Heaven and Hell, walking the pavements like goddesses through grass. Youth, youth,
I thought, fingering my grey chin and hearing distant wild,
sweet pipes. Alas, too close.

"The Bank of Spain," cried the taxi-driver, pointing at an
enormous white building. I paid him three hundred pesetas
and went inside. Five commissionaires, three special police,
two Civil Guards, four security police, and a few fully armed
soldiers approached me civilly and asked me my business.
This may have had something to do with my suit. I can only
wear any suit for about twenty-four hours, and after that I

235

should throw it away. It crumples, shrinks, and gets covered with soup, wine and olive oil. Dogs bite it, cats scratch it, and moths eat it. The pockets bulge with cigarette butts and handbills. "I want to see Antonio Vegas," I said. "Up the stairs to your right," said one of the armed police, pointing with his revolver. I climbed up miles of milk-white stairs and arrived at an enormous corridor which melted into a creamy distance. Everywhere were huge commissionaires and police with guns. I pattered down the infinite corridor, engulfed by a strange carpeted silence—such a silence as I had never heard before in Spain, where for every second of every day dogs bark, cats shriek, flies buzz, owls hoot, pigs squeal, women scream, children howl, and men curse. It was quieter than a cathedral; it was like being under the sea, or on top of a mountain. It was, I guessed, because of the enormous sanctity of so much money collected together in such a huge building. In England you *see* more money, it is thrown about, and dropped and waved and bandied about, and loses its fetish value, like, say, a woman's bosom. And it means less to more people, it doesn't mean Christ on the Cross and millions and millions of loaves of bread and sacks of garlic and children's shoes for a saint's day.

"I want to see Antonio Vegas," I said to a posse of policemen. "What is your business?" "I am the friend of a friend," I said mysteriously. "Señor Vegas is at the end of the corridor. You will find another corridor. Turn left and you will find yet another. Turn right and it is at the end." As I walked down the long sober avenues, I could see august anterooms full of people as motionless as sleeping princesses, turned to stone by the spell of five million thousand pesetas. "Where is Antonio Vegas?" I asked one of them, but he didn't hear me, he didn't see me. My suit made me invisible; he smelt my empty pockets like a ferret, his finger was on my unconvertible web of words.

"That is the room of Antonio Vegas," said a commission-aire, pointing at a door which said "Fiscal Sub-section." I opened the door and found myself in a small office which contained a desk and a woman seated at it. She had the usual bank face, the tubular body which could never be raped, the polished mahogany smile bereft of flowers, but was elegantly dressed. I do not know the position of Haute Couture in Spain, but I prefer the dresses of Spanish girls to any other in Europe. They are tulips and larkspurs and daffodils and fall from the waist like fountains. Suddenly, very often, all is lost, and winter sets in, and they become a shapeless black nest of memories.

"Señor Antonio Vegas?" "Certainly," she said, pointing at another door. "He is not engaged." I opened the door and found myself in a large, carpeted room with two ornate tables, a dictaphone, and a handsome glittering set of chandeliers. It might have been the room of a small dictator, a theatrical impresario, an ambitious doctor, or a best-selling novelist. Behind one of the desks was a plump bald man and beside him was a rather pretty woman in her thirties, with the bold gay face of a soldier intent on losing another battle. "Señor Vegas," I said, approaching the plump man, and holding out the letter. "I am he," he said, reading the letter. "Please seat yourself." When he had finished he offered me a cigarette and leant back in his chair. His face was bland, unwrinkled and unsanctified; it had no holy smell of the peseta. "So you are a writer," he said. "I too follow the arts in my spare time." "Indeed," I said. "Under another name, of course. Carlos Prieto. I play the bassoon for the wireless."

⊔⊓⊔⊓⊔⊓⊔⊓⊔⊓⊔⊓⊔⊓⊔⊓⊔

HOME SERVICE ABROAD

EVERYBODY WHO travels sincerely wants to lose himself. This of course can have disastrous consequences. On the other hand, travel without a certain amount of shipwreck is almost entirely pointless, a mere collection of casinos, hotels, chambermaids, processions and varying menus. When I arrived in Galicia I had a very strong desire to plunge and dissolve in the labyrinths of the country, into the mystical bars, the shadows of the saints, and the almost mythical bosoms of the women, softened by rain and mellow with fruit and fecundity. The idea of the erudite traveller scoffing up a parchment and denying himself the excesses of drink and the flesh, or the dreams of the flesh, or the sudden firework of the child, has always revolted me. The citizen of the world should not be a pedant, although unfortunately pedants are practically the only existing citizens of the world.

One day I arrived in a small town on a bay. The name of the town was Cobodon. It looked across a long stretch of water to a far-away stretch of land with those sort of golden bays which promise every kind of fulfilment. The sky was enormous, dappled with clouds of milk and butter, and the earth was purple and green and golden with a sun as soft as the tongue of a calf. I stayed there two days, exhilarated by the extraordinary fetish of the women road-menders. In the heart of Galicia is a dream of these extraordinary women, strong as bullocks, slender and firm as unripe pears, with eyes like cats in a full moon. I went to the edge of the town and watched them at work. They dug, broke stones, tunnelled earth, heaved at wheelbarrows, and sifted sand. Women workers have always appalled me, uniformed ladies in tube stations, stenographers on holiday, air-hostesses with film-star smiles, female politicians. But these are not so. Galicia, unlike the rest of Spain, is in the hands of women; there is a vast matriarchy at work. They are the purple and the green and the gold. I am no Don Juan, I am well past my prime, the days of the happy robber are over, but the vision of these glowing Stone Age women gripped me like the first terrifying pipes of the *Rites of Spring*.

One day, in the clutch of this primitive dream, I was standing at the port of Cobodon, watching girls load barrels of vinegar, when I was approached by three men and a girl in a neat tartan frock.

"Excuse me," one of them said, the tallest, in a neat black suit with an open-collared shirt, "but you are English?" He spoke the language with a terrible kind of laboured perfection, the grammar was back to front but horribly perfect.

"Certainly," I said.

"This I have definitely heard," he said, "and I wish you to introduce yourself to Elspeth, a Scotch young lady, who is the children's teacher of this gentleman, Don Alfredo." He indicated a smaller, neater man with a long, eager nose. "She has arrived from the town of Perth, just."

Elspeth was a bright keen girl like a civic tulip, all smiles in a new land. Friendship, not mere acquaintanceship, is made at meteor speed in Galicia, it is like a blood transfusion, you are never the same again. You can never leave anybody, a whole town follows you, people appear like magicians, songs creep into your ear.

"This is a poor town, Cobodon," said the first speaker, whose name was Mario. "It has no education. The women work like bullocks. A terrible affair. Come to Noya. It is over there."

He pointed across the water. It seemed a good idea. You can't write about Galicia without smelling the bays, the fish, the boats, the weather on the waves. The Stone Age girls? That study could be left till later. I could ask Mario about them discreetly.

I collected my luggage and we met on the wharf. The boat was a large launch with a huge funnel, the sort of craft which had seen a revolution or two in tropical creeks, and smelt of shellfish. For some reason or other there were about sixteen people there, and we all clambered into the boat, the whistle hooted, the engines chugged and we were off. At once everybody started singing, and a dog ran up and down the boat like a second mate. I looked at the beautiful charged sky, the glittering water and the heather-coloured mountains, like a man in a myth. I didn't want to take my eyes off the scene.

"Sir," said a voice at my side. It was Mario. He was smoking a pipe.

"Ah," I said, my eyes going back to the mountains.

"Have you seen Hampton Court?"

"Why, yes," I said.

"And Windsor Castle?"

"I have," I said.

"And Buckingham Palace?"

"Certainly," I said.

"How fortunate," he said with a sigh.

"This is very beautiful," I said, pointing over the bay.

"It is boring and monotonous," said Mario, knocking out his pipe, "but the fish are passable."

There was a pause. Everybody was singing "I'll See You in My Dreams" in Spanish. It sounded incredibly melancholy, echoing over the water like a chant for the drowned. This seemed to be the time to drop a hint about Stone Age girls.

"Sociologically speaking," I began, "the subject of peasant women in Galicia presents striking features."

"Oh," said Mario, refilling his pipe.

"The girls, for instance, seem to begin working at an early age. I was wondering where, for instance——"

"They are animals," said Mario. "We are far behind the times, you know. Transport, and so on. Heating. Have you ever entered Buckingham Palace actually?"

"No," I said.

"But is not there a tea-party there?"

"Yes, but I've never been invited," I said, trying to drop the subject and looking back at the mountains.

"In Hampton Court . . ." continued Mario.

The skipper and Elspeth's employer came over and joined us. They spoke English. You could see that the idea of England fascinated them—fog, *The Times*, enormous policemen, strange jokes, rigid silences, horses, dogs, and everyone shouting in Hyde Park. It was an obvious, sincere admiration, and I was sorry to be a completely inadequate specimen.

After an hour or two the whistle hooted and I could see the launch heading straight for the bank at full speed. I could hardly believe my eyes. The dog dropped its role as second mate and ran to the scuppers cowering with terror. Everybody stopped singing.

"What's happened?" I asked Mario.

"It's all right," he said. "The tide's out at Noya. We're landing here, in a manner of saying. Then we ambulate for approximately four miles."

The launch hit a bank of shingle with a tremendous jolt, we jumped on to the ground, girls were helped down, luggage thrown out, including under-water apparatus, five salmon and a motor-bicycle. The dog took charge again, trotting off in front as busy as a beadle, and everybody began singing. I couldn't see my luggage. The country was wild and wooded and at that time of dusk packed with fairies. You could almost see their eyes shining through the bracken. I bitterly longed for youth again, and the wild gardens.

"I have written an essay about St. George's Chapel in Windsor," said Mario, walking at my side. "When we reach Noya I would like to demonstrate it to you."

"Thank you," I said. It was getting darker and the clouds were mauve.

"It is for the B.B.C. English Competition. Home Service."

The dog started to bark at a rabbit.

"How is it?" shouted the skipper in English.

"Fine," I cried in a typical Windsor voice.

THE DUEL

I HAVE never heard of a student of bagpipes, but I suppose such a thing exists, since nearly everybody is a student of something. When I arrived in Galicia, I was very surprised to discover that bagpipes formed the greater part of the national music, and decided, with the help of wine, aguardiente, brandy, anis, and extraordinarily cheap champagne cocktails, to make a study of them. The flower of bagpipe time is during the feast of the Apostle in Santiago de Compostela, when groups of players accompanied by a man with a tiny drum march through the streets playing tamed Celtic airs. They are dressed in breeches, red stockings, and flutter with ribbons, the great gourd of their pipes slung over their shoulders like a haunch of venison. But it is a sad procession, unwitnessed and unloved, like a robin singing in a cemetery. The people of Santiago are praying or drinking, their great red-haired gods sulking in the mists of the mountains, and nobody gives a damn.

I hadn't been long in Santiago before I met a man called Jonathan Speed. He was a plump man with far-away belligerent eyes who had come to Galicia to study cathedrals. But it was obvious that he was in search of something else, a private phantom, a strange unedited solution.

One day we heard some bagpipes. They were as wild as wind in the heather, stark with the naked cries of happy murderers in the glens, as Scotch as haggis, or as Irish as promises. "Astounding," said Speed, "to hell with cathedrals and progressive jazz. Let us buy bagpipes."

Somebody told us about a master bagpipe manufacturer called Pablo. He made the bagpipes in front of your very eyes as another man makes hats or cigars. And when he had fluted the bagpipes he put the pipe to his lips and Pan blazed in the shop. Pan, and no other. Wonderful, insuperable, lost Pan. "The very thing," said Speed, and we went to the shop with one of those eternal Spanish friends who hunt for you everything from sardines to saints. There, in a lost street, crumpled with children, we entered a shop sweet with new sharpened wood, the hum of a lathe, and the royal red blaze of the bagpipe blowers.

"Make me a bagpipe," said Speed.

"And me a bagpipe without the bag," I said.

In half an hour the bagpipes were on the counter and in another quarter of an hour I had a pipe as gay as a tinker's donkey. Speed slung the bag over his shoulder, blew on the pipe, there was a roar like a stuck pig, and a tune came out as brave as a field in May. It was a Northumbrian air, but it made no difference. I blew on my pipe and there was nothing but the wind. "Dance," said Speed, so I danced a vague Hibernian dance, and the children scuttled into the shop and Pablo himself raised the fluted pipe to his mouth and the sawdust room was a world of glow-worms. Later we went from feast to feast until one day he suddenly put on a black suit and a homburg hat and left for England. "My work," he said. Poetry or progressive jazz or cathedrals? I didn't ask him. I am English, but I don't understand the English.

I was alone with the pipe. I started to blow it in my small hotel high up above the Civil Guards, the commercial travellers, the pigs and the hens and the bells. I blew and I blew and not a note came out, just a sound like wind in the wainscoting, like old men coughing over their pipes in a ruined dormitory. I packed my bags, paid my bill and left for the village of Ribeira at the end of a bay and went up into the hills. "Look out for wolves, eagles and ghosts," said an old female domestic who occasionally threw a bucket of water into the Stone Age latrine. She told me about an eagle which had killed an elderly councillor in the town hall. "It sat outside the window and stared at him," she said. "He died of fright." They came from Portugal and might be dead relatives.

Up in the hills were wonderful wild flowers and tiny bees so industrious that they made you ashamed. I blew on the pipe and certain notes rang on the air like drowned bells. There are seven apertures on the pipe, unevenly placed, and the fingers have to be as nimble as spiders. Also the breath must flow like a great slow bellows, and the head hold a discipline of harmony, born and slowly learnt. The first pattern of music was a small broken Moorish melody; it got itself caught in the pipe on its way from Marrakesh or the tinkling markets of Tiznit. I played this tune over and over again and got stung by a bee. This was not what I sought. I craved the lilt of the early Galician days, when Irish giants sat on their thrones and the story-tellers sat under the cedars. And at last, among the wild lilies and the heather, a minute gasping melody flowed from the pipe. I do not know how. I don't necessarily believe in inspiration and wouldn't care to state that there are obvious reasons for everything. We all have the secret ground which is ourselves—it runs counter to so many orthodox arguments. For me, writing is a certain craft which matures through repetition, but sometimes, in painting, about which I know nothing, I can capture the whole of a small world in a few seconds.

I repeated this pattern of notes, and lay back on the heather.

A seagull floated over my head but did not speak. About ten minutes later I heard a flurry over the grass, a rustling, and a pattern of horn and hoof, and looked around. I was surrounded by sheep. Roughly there must have been about five hundred, which meant a thousand eyes, perplexed, inquiring and cold with the cold doubt of sheep. They stood there, ciphers of wool and mutton, with a blaze in their brains. I have never heard of a man being attacked by sheep, but who could tell? I remembered about the eagles and ghosts and stood up. Far away I could hear a man shouting, and presently saw him, a black figure with a looming face. He was waving a pipe, the same fluted shape as mine, and suddenly he sat down, put it to his lips and blew. There was tremble in the wind, a spell of silver and sunlight, and the sheep teetered on their hooves, flickered their eyes and disappeared. I sat down and looked at the pipe. It held a fascinating power. It was impossible to resist it. I put it to my lips and blew and the notes scampered over the heather like hares on a bright morning. I hadn't long to wait. In another minute the sheep were back, ringing me round with a wild, thin, staring hope. I was the new Messiah of a grassy Salvation. Again I could hear the man shouting, and I got up and walked back to the village, and entered the inn and began drinking at the bar.

"A good day?" asked the proprietor, polishing the glasses.

"A good day," I said. "I've learnt to play a tune on the bagpipe."

"Play it," said the proprietor with a laugh.

I lifted the pipe to my lips and the notes fell out of it like dice.

"I never heard a tune like that," said the proprietor, filling my glass.

It was about five minutes later that the first of the sheep trotted into the inn.

ELEGY TO A DEAD DOG

IGNACIO TORRES had a studio at the top of a high house in Paloma, south of Barcelona. Room wandered to room, packed with hangings, ironwork, oil paintings, glazed earthenware jars, crockery, gourds and mirrors, and ended at a breathless red and ochre roofscape framed in a window. You had to gasp, there were so many mysterious roofs, and the sky was as blue as a ribbon.

Ignacio Torres was a small man. He was so furious at not being taller that he used to jump up and down when he was alone, shaking his fists at the roofs. He was a builder and decorator, but he could smell divinity in shapes and colours, and what he saw flashed in his mind like a diamond. He also painted landscapes and portraits very badly. The spark failed and he made up for this by designing enormous murals in the castles of profiteers, high up on long ladders like a monkey, throwing out his chest. Only thus was he a tall man.

When he was not in his studio, or his castles, or his house, he turned himself into a buffoon. He capered about the streets, or sat in the Café Lux making faces at people. The police never interfered with him, because he was labelled "Artist." In Spain the madness of the artist, if not his wisdom, is sacrosanct. He formed part of a *tertulia*, or group, and stabbed each friend in the back with a sharp, invisible knife. At night he sat in the open-air nightclub and watched the dancers, hate in his heart. Only once I saw him dancing himself, and that was with a minute woman whom he whirled around like a top, clearing the floor.

One night I was sitting with him in the club watching a dance by a pair of synthetic Barcelona gypsies when a peculiar dog strolled on to the floor. It paused there bathed in the spotlight. It was a composite sort of dog with a high tail and back-street ears, and did not appear so much lost as misdirected. "There's Tani," cried Ignacio at the top of his voice. "Tani, Tani!" The dog looked up and strolled slowly over to our table, with the slight haste of a late guest. It lay down under the table and closed its eyes.

"Is this your dog?" I asked Ignacio.

"Certainly not," he said. "He is no one's dog. He is a poet, a philosopher, a *torero*. He sometimes stays with me, sometimes with the ragman near the cathedral, or with the priest of San Roman, or in a brothel by the tobacco factory, but mostly he sleeps in the street. I always know where he is because the children tell me, or the police, or the postman." Ignacio bent down and peered at the dog. "It is strange," he continued, "but he is not sleeping, he is thinking." While Ignacio looked at the dog his eyes were gentle and his voice was soft. This amazed me. In Spain you do not expect to find random sentimentality connected with animals; there is no emotional projection into fur, hide or feathers.

"Do you like dogs very much?"

"Not *dogs*," answered Ignacio, "any more than I like *people*. I suppose all Spaniards are excited by the idea of liberty, because we have so little of it, and I am attracted towards the Don Quixote in this animal. He refuses to conform, he strolls airily along the pavements, he has his salt, he chooses his friends, he even escapes from conventional doggery. He doesn't even bark." Later we went down below to the café, followed by the dog, and everybody in the *tertulia* patted him, and Tani curled himself up and thought.

A week later a boy got bitten by a dog. The dog had rabies. The next day another boy got bitten by a dog. The Paloma radio station, after announcing the triumphal opening of a new bus station in Galicia, attended by the Caudillo, made a statement about dogs. The voice of the announcer was slightly hysterical; he almost seemed to be barking. All dogs had to be registered, identified, documented, inoculated, and any dogs without visible means of support would be summarily destroyed. *Arriba España, Viva Franco.*

When I saw Ignacio that evening he was still playing the buffoon. Nothing is more important to Spaniards than saving face, than talking round the sword. All the *tertulia* talked around the sword, until Ignacio slipped up to the nightclub to outstare the dancers, and they told me the truth. Tani couldn't be found. He hadn't been to the beach, to the church of San Roman, to the brothel or the rag shop. He had to be found immediately, in order to be registered, documented, inoculated and transformed into a civic dog. Ignacio had procured and filled in the necessary papers, had bought an identity disc, and made a date with the dog doctor.

Later that night the ragman appeared at the café. "Tani is in prison," he said. "He has been condemned to death."

"By whom?" shouted Ignacio, in the voice of a giant.

"By the Mayor," answered the ragman.

At once all the *tertulia* rose to their feet. The group was composed of diverse and conflicting trends, Fatherland the Falangist reporter, Antonio the rebel conscript, businessmen, idlers, fathers of families, students. Without saying a word, Ignacio marched from the café and we followed, up the street from the sea, under a moon like a silver spider, across the Avenue of Generalissimo Franco, past the crouching cathedral, to the house of his Excellency the Mayor. Ignacio knocked at the door, and a woman opened it.

"I demand to see the Mayor," he shouted.

"His Excellency is busy," said the woman. She was quite tall, and she looked down on the furious little builder like a tree.

"He's not too busy to see that justice is done," he cried.

At this a stout man, quite bald, appeared in the doorway, wiping shreds of lobster from his mouth with a napkin. "What do you want?" he asked, peering forward at our faces.

"The release of Tani," said Ignacio.

"Who or what is Tani?" asked the Mayor.

"He is a dog," replied Ignacio.

"A dog? A dog?" cried the Mayor, suddenly roaring with laughter.

"You imprisoned him," said Ignacio, trembling all over.

"What if I did?" said the Mayor, still laughing. "I am defending the safety of the public. Children, defenceless women, the aged. I will not let a single vagabond dog imperil them. He shall be destroyed. It is my duty. Good night!"

He shut the door, and we could still hear his laughter, like grasshoppers rattling in a box.

The next morning Ignacio visited the dogs' pound with a jug of milk and some bones. The dog died at six, but from the expression on Ignacio's face you would never have known it. The local paper, *Hoy*, came out with a magnificent obituary from which it appeared that Tani had once had an owner from whom he had run away—the Mayor.

PART FOUR

⌐_⌐_⌐_⌐_⌐_⌐_⌐_⌐_⌐_⌐_

GOING SOUTH

WE STARTED OFF with a fairly old, extremely tough Lambretta, an orange-coloured tent, sleeping-bags, a Woolworth methy-lated stove, a suitcase containing unsmart serviceable clothes, a blanket, plastic crockery, a frying-pan, two books of poems, and eggs and coffee from N.12. We arrived in Calais after a flat, unatmospheric trip and disembarked. It was raining. There was no difference in this and London rain. Everybody endlessly rained on looks the same, they crouch in a similar way, cough and make desperate jokes. We had to move from Calais Port to Calais Town, and set off by the Lambretta. We stopped half-way at a café. Inside there was a juke box and a notice saying BACEN AND EGS. We sat there for about an hour, drinking relatively cheap wine, putting coins in the universal song-machine, and looking at the rain.

"It's not very foreign," said Mart.

"It'll change," I said.

"How do you know?" she said.

"There's a sort of line," I said. "It's actually a distinct line demarcating the northern weather from the southern. Below that line the weather has its own rules. Even now, in October, people are swimming down there and picking grapes."

253

When we reached Calais Town railway station, we had to buy tickets and make arrangements to have the Lambretta shipped to Paris. Our destination was Arles. This meant that an official must weigh the machine, and he began to begin the operations. He looked at the Lambretta with immense dislike and pointed to the scales. The way he pointed made everyone in the baggage office stare at the Lambretta and us. "This is the North of France," I said. "It's quite different in the South. These people are grocers and limp traditionalists." As a matter of fact the machine had an extraordinary aspect, something of Giacometti with colour by a drunken Pre-Raphaelite. I heard the official talking to members of the crowd about it. He referred to it as a "travelling brothel." A woman with neat hair and a competently-cut beige ensemble tittered, not too much and not too little, just right; she was obviously married to someone in the Town Hall. I stood beside her at the ticket office staring at her, hating her, hating her in depth, right back to her careful great-great-grandmother and her hypocritical great-great-grandfather.

After a hateful journey, stopping at tiny, rainy stations, we arrived in Paris. It was an enormous relief. Paris is full of crooks, childish people, eccentrics, solitaries, saints and the selfish rich, all covered over by a construction of great, logical beauty. It has changed its soul six or seven times since I used to live there, before the war, but its skin is exactly the same, good to the touch. We have friends in Paris, but even breathing is costly there. We drove (through the rain) past the Bastille to the Gare de Lyon, bought tickets to Avignon, shipped the Lambretta into the baggage truck, all witnessed by men of tact and good will, and sped off towards the line of demarcation. There, in the carriage, I suddenly realised I was very ill. I could hardly breathe, my head was aching, and I was sweating violently. Possibly I was at my last gasp; only my corpse would arrive in the happy zone of sunshine.

The night was through neatly, and there was Avignon. We
hung around the railway station, south of the demarcation
line, and, sure enough, the air was soft and the sky like a bright
shore with pools of blue. We had coffee and stacked up the
Lambretta and set off for Arles. To first see the tree-lined
avenues of Arles is like meeting your true love, still young
and unhurt, after agonies of time. (I had, as a matter of fact,
seen Arles twenty-five years ago, travelling on a push bicycle.)
We stayed stationary in the spell, found a hotel, and had lunch.
We took some time choosing a restaurant, preferably a work-
man's restaurant, and finally settled on a pleasurably ruined
house, rose-roofed, with faded, oblique windows. Inside were
neat tables dotted with doilies, and a pear-shaped homosexual
verging on the sixties, with the sort of face more connected
with the crafts than the arts. On a wall behind our table was a
pasted-on collection of reproductions of Van Gogh, obviously
cut out of *Paris-Match*, and Mart interested herself looking at
them. I don't really like Van Gogh, he makes Provence look
hysterical, but he is certainly wonderful with roots and potatoes, and this without irony. "He used to eat here," said the
pear-shaped man, rubbing his ivory hands. We then studied
the menu, which abounded in Provençal dishes: *Riz à la Arlé-
sienne, Hot-pot à la Gardien*, roughly translated as Hot-pot
á la Camargue Cowboy, and *Snails au cours libre*, or snails in
the fashion of the Camargue bullfight. It looked delicious, and
we ordered rice, hot-pot and snails.

Tiny dishes arrived like saucers. "The hot-pot," said pear-
shape, "is *délicieuse*, a special recipe." Another tiny saucer
arrived, and some very usual regional bread. "Real French
bread," hissed pear-shape. Mart got angry before I did; I was
too ready to carry on the magic introduction to Arles, I was
ready to swallow Van Gogh and the tiny saucers. After the
meal, we rose and it was set upon me to make a speech. "I now
understand," I said, "why Van Gogh cut off his ear. He ate

here!" Pear-shape bowed like an ageing tree before the mistral. He said nothing. All his words were saved for the summer coach-tours, and the underpaid washer-up.

At night Arles folded up. The cafés didn't like you after ten o'clock, and the next morning we drove off to Tarascon. I have never read *Tartarin*, but we stayed in a hotel of the same name. The meals were colossal and the cheapest I have ever known in France. After dinner we drove off to a café in the centre and drank *pastis*. Then the storm broke. Lightning, thunder and explosions were continuous, and the rain fell from the sky like ruins. The power station was struck three times and all the lights went out. The people in the café sang all the time. There was a very pretty girl serving behind the counter and there were a certain number of screams and suddenly the lights went up, the girl's face was bright with roses and the floor was covered with soldiers' caps. Then the lights went out again, and the songs were softer, the screams muffled and by the time the lights went on again there was no girl at all, there was an angular woman in spectacles.

"I'm sorry about the interruptions," she said to us.

"Not at all," we said. "It makes us feel at home."

We were looking for a home. We were looking for a home round about this area, where Picasso painted, where the invalids came, where the dawn first milked the sky after the dark ages, where the croupiers sang with the owls and the nightingales, where the shell-fish glistened in the early blue-eyed market. We drove to Aix. This is the most civilised town in Provence; you could meet Cocteau in any of the bars, or Stravinsky or Buffet at a *vernissage*. It is a southern Paris and, apart from the corrupted Riviera, the only Provençal town animated by fashion. We couldn't find an apartment there because of the students. They filled the town like autumn butter-flies, quite as beautiful and far harder working than their English equivalents, but soon destined for unspecified massacre.

"What about Poppet?" said Mart. Poppet was a woman who lived somewhere on the Riviera. Her address had been given to us in London, accompanied by a note, by her sister. Unfortunately this sister wrote terribly badly and couldn't really spell. The address appeared to be Vance. We looked at the map and asked questions and found a place called Vence in the Alpes Maritimes above Nice. This meant driving down to the sea-coast and we picked on St. Tropez, "because of Brigitte Bardot," said Mart. "Possibly," I said. The newspapers were full of suicide and film directors in dark glasses waiting at airports and nightclub singers meeting other singers' or directors' wives and the latest bulletin said they were walking up and down St. Tropez holding hands. "Actually there's a super-director behind the lot," said Mart. "The French only get excited about food and money." All the same, she had a strange doom-like feeling about my meeting Bardot, by moonlight, against a backcloth of palms, speaking perfect argot.

We arrived at St. Tropez in the late evening. It smelled of new francs, and the harbour was crammed with yachts people had lost or swapped. Everything was so obviously expensive, people went about dressed like tramps. It was eating time, and through the twinkling crystal windows you could see lobsters glowing like rubies and the pearls falling out of the oysters. "Bardot and the directors will be in there," said Mart, looking at me with a slight contempt. We drove a little way out of St. Tropez and found a camping site. It was an organised affair with lavatories, running water, showers, refuse bins and a shop, and was dotted with pine trees. We set up the orange tent, boiled some coffee and tried to go to sleep on the hard floor of sand. Next door, in another tent, two young Germans talked interminably, snipping up the night into sharp gutturals. It was like someone throwing stones. At about two o'clock in the morning it started to rain. It rained very steadily and then it began to pour. Two hours later it was a decent sort

of cloudburst. The Germans, their deep talk ceased, set themselves to dig trenches. We could hear the Lambretta collapse
on the ground, accompanied by a splash. Mart, who did everything, went out into the roaring night, retrieved the machine,
and also started digging. The tent was now full of mosquitoes,
seeking food and shelter, and through the flap I could see a
sort of lake.

It was still raining when we packed up. Mart somehow managed to make some coffee and cook some eggs and we made
for St. Raphael and Cannes. Sometimes the rain stopped, and
we stopped at various half-packed pleasure villages and
watched the tumbling purple sea. These places were, now, out
of season, quite anonymous, old women haggling over the
kitchen poetry of tomatoes, a shirt-sleeved bunch playing
cards, one or two unhappy tourists mooning at postcards with
no one to send them to, a magnificent policeman holding up
winter. Cannes wasn't much brighter but longer, whiter. The
rain came down, and we went into a restaurant to have a meal.
Mart felt very exhausted, mainly because she always drove the
Lambretta and because of the terrible load of odds and ends
the machine carried, with more objects being acquired en
route. But the surprise restaurant meals always cheered her
up, and myself as well, because they invariably freshened and
amazed. Ingenuity is the only real virtue of the French.

Between Cannes and Nice one turns inland to reach Vence.
The road up is steep with a flurry of vines, a brood of pines
and castle crannies. The air is now warm, now cold, languor-
ous or ice-whipped. We both had a feeling we were somehow
coming home. At such moments, half nomadic, mazed by
changing views, one looks at the people in the street with a
kind of mania, everyone has to give immediate signals and in-
dications of enormous nobility, generosity and a special sort
of wit. We went into a restaurant bar ("terribly friendly,"
we said) and were served with wine by a pretty waitress

("what exquisite manners," we said). I asked her about Poppet's address and showed her the note written by her sister.

"You're in the wrong region," said the waitress. "It should be Vars. It's miles away. Somewhere near St. Tropez." In the corner of the note I saw a telephone number. The waitress helped me ring it up, but there was no such number. Poppet's sister really was rather vague. We drank our wine and looked at each other. This couldn't go on. Stoves, thunderstorms, back-street hotels, hot words stored in water-proof bags, on and on.

"We'll live here?" I said.

"We'll live here," said Mart.

The world, whatever it may really be, soon shrinks into a kitchen, a double bed, and the weather in the windows.

THE GRIMM COAST

VENCE IS a sober spot, half-way between small town and village, pigeon grey, sly with arches, and linked by a whispering plot of fountains. In the main tree-heavy square you can sit in the autumn sunshine, still burning like a half-coiled iron, sip *pastis* and read the local newspapers. One called *La Patriote* is communist, and at the time of our arrival it was throwing huge over-ripe verbal tomatoes at General de Gaulle, who was appearing on a southern visit, leaning, like the Tower of Pisa, over mayors and minors. On one side of this square is a rather smart but modest bar called Pierre's Bar. For one day, with the help of the Syndicat d'Initiative, we had been hunting for furnished rooms, and had given up when an elderly lady, the owner of a residence called the Poet's Nest, had firmly closed the door in our noses. "It is a pity," said Mart, "because it would have been a good address." Now, after a woman's radar look, she decided Pierre would solve our problems.

This was true. Pierre was a true Provençal, thin and yellow as lemon peel, wrestling with some gnawing rat of an illness, man of all trades, married to a rather commanding lady who loved small talk and the discreet accumulation of money. We went in. There were a few people in the bar, elderly, well-off, artistic, who, you felt, had made a hard bargain for giving up. "I have furnished rooms," said Pierre, "and all mod. cons." The price was sixteen thousand francs a month. "Yes," we said immediately, even before viewing. We were shown around by Pierre. The flat was on the third floor, two rooms, soft Provençal view, good intimate furnishing and colour, running hot water from a *Butagaz*, installation for washing-up, basin and bidet, own private modern lavatory.

The first night's sleeping was like a long convalescence. We were woken up twice round about dawn by a soft eruption of turtle-doves. This was strange, even magic, because Pierre's surname was Tortorolo which in Niçois or Italian means "turtle-dove." Pierre Turtledove. When we woke up properly it was raining, an even more hopeless rain than the old London spittle, and we looked out of the windows at the weeping trees and the curling white breath of the mountains. The land looked like a beaten woman and the turtle-doves cried her shame. There they were, in fact, in the garden below us, eight of them. Four of them were flattened on the windowsills, two immolated on a roof top, the other pair copulating.

We had a morning drink at Pierre's. He talked about people. Marc Chagall used to live here and an Englishman called Lawrence. He was here, near the railway station, three or four years. During this period he wrote a book, *The Lover of Lady Chatterley*. No, he hadn't read it, Madame did all the reading. Lawrence died in this very place. He used to come into his bar again and again. No, he couldn't really remember him, he was one of the crowd. The sun came out; Mart went shopping; I sat in the square reading the *Patriote*. There was a front-page rear-attack on de Gaulle, and the rest of the paper was given up to murders, except for an outcry against a proposal to drop radio-active material into the Mediterranean between Corsica and St. Raphael. All the murders were well documented and had the air of being written by an ingenious but mad film director of the thirties. They mostly occurred in lonely farmhouses. Monsieur N, for instance, had been clubbed and throttled to death by his wife, children and father-in-law, after muddling up some sheep while the worse for drink. The family group then *sat down to a late lunch* before the father-in-law telephoned the police. Then Monsieur V, owing to family troubles, had written to the local paper and police, informing them that he was on the point of committing suicide, and gratefully *leaving his house appurtenances and utensils to the Superintendent.* Monsieur V's house was immediately surrounded by firemen and other officials, but there was no Monsieur V. He telephoned a few minutes later from a near-by village, apologising for the trouble, but the walls were porous and the gas had escaped. General relief was expressed, but Monsieur V (this actually occurred in the next issue) returned home and shot himself, leaving a note which *again left his household goods to the Superintendent.* Some grim comic relief was provided by an elderly farm-labourer out for a shot who hid himself in a bush and imitated a blackbird. Unfortunately a sporting taxi-driver was after this very bird and shot the farm-labourer in the face. All, however, ended well, reported the paper, since the pellets were easily removed and the labourer was *able to return to work the same afternoon.*

We travelled down to Nice on the Lambretta. You can freewheel down a quarter of the way. In the middle of the journey is a valley with a sea of vines and olives and beaches of earth pricked to blood by the hoe. Rising from the flecked sea are islands tapering to shipwrecked castles and towns, grey, rose-headed mariners clinging like limpets to the rock. There is a curd of morning smoke and a muffled bell taps the sky. Here we stopped, and in fine weather we always stopped. A few days later, over these sleeping leagues of Fairyland, an eagle swung in the sky, black as an exiled king, slow as retribution, and the frame in our eyes was cut deep with wonder. Below is the village of Cagnes, but between are pockets of heat and cold like the hands of friends or strangers, and a flurry of early smells, the dark bosoms of beech and thin pine fingers kissed by the sun.

Then here was Nice, and the old holiday sea, blue as a new school exercise-book. The same old Nice, creamy, vulgar, out of time, bitter-sweet with the ghosts of dead monarchs and brilliant prostitutes, edging past grubby grandeur to the old sleeping port. This, and Paris, were my old ruined pavilions, and I could catch the taste of dead dreams on my tongue like spray. We parked the Lambretta opposite the Negresco, and went to the beach to have a swim. Amazing bedlam rocked in our eyes. The sea boiled with waves, they galloped to the walls and spumed over the Promenade des Anglais. A huge crowd had collected. There were firemen and policemen and ambulances, and the eyes of the spectators were hard with disaster. They all had that neat look of Mediterranean people to whom nothing could ever happen, the chosen sane, the uncuckolded, unrobbed, sheltered from disease and accident by doctors, God and the municipality. Yet, any time now, the bell would ring for them, the gilded love-house, the mad grandmother or the bloody child at the crossroads. Mart, too, was sucked into the crowd, not because she felt immune from public horror, but because the world was always ending, except in bed. I joined her, a sort of queasy journalist. Far out at sea we could see a circular rubber object with a body on it. The body was the colour of rotten marble.

"It's a woman," said Mart. A boat was approaching it, and someone in oilskins leant over the boat and fell in. It was accidental, but nobody in the crowd made a sound, as though the world was an infamous church. Then two men grappled on to the marble body and dragged it on to the boat. It was growing cold. We left the crowd and drove back to Vence.

Half-way, before eagle valley, the cool evening perfumes stood beckoning at the corners of the roads. Mart is unable to smell, her sense organs were impaired years ago, and I had to explain the low, sharp, sweet signals in the air. When we got back home we felt exhausted. London sickness (a sort of guilt, sandwiches and the incestuous Soho pubs) still numbed our brains and bodies. We went straight to bed and slept until the turtle-doves drummed up the startling October sun.

The next morning, in the square opposite Pierre's, I read about the Nice beach catastrophe in the *Patriote*. Mart had been right, the body had been a woman's. It belonged to a Madame N. Enquiries had been made in the neighbourhood, and it transpired that Madame N's husband had made an arrangement with the dead lady's sister to launch together into the strong sea and there leave Madame N to perish. The sister, able to swim, had returned to the shore, but instead of returning to her brother-in-law (with whom she had an illicit relationship), she went to her fiancé's house and confessed everything. Her fiancé reported her to the police, and then jumped off a cliff near Monte Carlo.

LOOKING FOR A GORGE

VENCE IS not far from Nice, yet the climate is entirely different, something like Switzerland, but also sheltered. As Pierre said, D. H. Lawrence lived here for three years on account of his health, and Mart and I began to notice numbers of people like discarded puppets, their old wires too far stretched, moving gently to the new, pristine electricity. There was actually a bar, in a side street, walled with bamboo, mostly frequented by sick miners. They came from a huge sanatorium (referred to by the townspeople affectionately as the "Sana"), about two hundred or so of them at a time, and staying in Vence for a minimum of three months. Since alcohol is extremely dangerous to people suffering from silicosis, they are only allowed out, on the town, for certain hours on Thursdays and Sundays, and on those days the Caveau Gambetta is a rolling, raucous holiday from hygienic dormitories and corridors of coal.

There is not only the special air, there is the water. It comes from a spring, somewhere up in the mountains, called La Foux, and appears in at least two places in the town, one under the archway which leads to the town hall and the post-office, gushing from two pipes, and the other beside a sort of beautiful

265

ruined church near Maison Tortorols, where we lived. The fountain of La Foux, which is under the archway, has a large information board over it:

TEMPERATURE—14 degrees
ASPECT   —limpid
ODOUR   —none
TASTE   —agreeable.

Its electricity resistancy at eighteen degrees is 3.630 ohms. In evaluation of organic matter, oxalic acid stands at 3.94, and permanganate of potash in oxygen 0.5. Its ions comprise sodium 1.95, calcium 47.10, magnesium 12.85, chlorine 3.00, sulphate 9.00 and silicate hydrate 5.85. There was other information, but it was too obscure and technical for me in any language, but obscure enough to stimulate me. While I was standing beside the fountain I saw ordinary people of the town fill bottles and jugs at the gushing pipe, not miners or partially resurrected foreigners but old women with string bags from the alleyways, the bakery assistant with reassuring rosy cheeks and an old spry man who might have been ninety.

I had often dreamed and mused about springs, as the ancients sailed great seas for fleeces or apples. This was due to a deep dissatisfaction with myself, a constant desire to change, and a longing to recapture youth by magic means. It also gave me a definite, though secret, order to my nomadic wanderings, here, there and everywhere. I mentioned the spring to Mart, and she was also impressed. I showed her the information from the chart, which I had copied down, but at once, I think, the number of chemicals, the electric resistancy and the exact decimals resolved themselves into a recipe for Olympian beauty. I filled an empty wine bottle from one of the pipes and put it in the kitchen. For lunch we had *moules marinières*, the recipe for which we had extracted from Pierre. You clean the mussels with wire wool, put them in a saucepan, heat the saucepan, and the mussels open—"obviously," added Pierre with delight. All Mediterranean people relish persecuting crustaceans. Then you mix and mince parsley, garlic and onion and construct a sauce. You pour the mussel liquid through a sieve and (apparently) add the sauce to it.

When the dish was ready we sat at the table and drank a few glasses of spring water, and then went for the mussels and their soup. The taste was absolutely horrible, it was a sort of Dead Sea Soup, but I am the sort of person who goes on eating what is definitely supposed to be good, and I swallowed at least six appalling mouthfuls. Mart stopped at once. She is unable to smell, but her taste organs are all the more powerful. A few minutes later my stomach gave me a warning, I felt cold and hot, and then I was gripped by the jaws of a terrible pain. "Take some more spring water," said Mart. I drank another two glasses and then the pain became almost unbearable. "It can't be the mussels," said Mart, "or all the Midi would be doubled up." No, it was the spring water. I looked at the information chart again and read, "electricity resistancy at eighteen degrees is 3.630 ohms." It reassured me a little, but the agony persisted. I went to bed.

It started to rain. The sky and the mountains were completely blotted out. The rain fell from a huge cold ocean in the sky; the bottom had fallen out. It rained for two days. The turtle-doves were silent as ivory tombs, and I went on drinking spring water. The pain was so great that I couldn't lie on my left side. But I refused to lose my faith in this panacea in which magic and science so exactly met, where the body was reborn through ohms from the thighs of enchanted mountains. As the pain subsided, thought flew to the brain, and Mart and I began to row, the ohms crackled in recriminations and private lightning filled the room. The world is despair, huge figures made of newspaper menace the poor just world, forces not merely evil but implacably cold shake all our foundations, money and truth never meet, work is the day's window-dressing and only poets and lunatics can stagger through the utterly unfurnished reception rooms of the night. Love must be insured, buttressed and inspected constantly with the eyes of spiders, the ears of bats; we must be we. Mart was heavy with London, and responsibilities she felt she had relinquished for palms, and the pride of sunshine; she wasn't here. It rained.

She stared at postcards and tried to copy them. "Like an old lady," I shouted. One husband had slipped talent into her nerve; another had, like a poacher, slowly wrung its neck. But it must sing. And then I, through the regiments of rain, stared at the white paper, afraid to decorate or disfigure it, a great cohort of idiot faces piled over my shoulder. Ghosts are more real than men or women. The rain stopped. Suddenly, one morning, it was a day of summer, the palms clapped their Egyptian hands and the sun danced in splendour. I went to open the door and was met by a Siamese cat with a collar and bell round its neck. It didn't look at me or at Mart but proceeded on an important state inspection; you could hear the drum, trumpets and the clang of rifle butts. It inspected the table-legs, tried a kitchen chair, sniffed at the carpet, tested the bed, examined under the kitchen stove, and peered into the lavatory bowl. Then it paused in the centre of the room. Something in its eye suggested all was well, but a bit more effort was needed. Then it walked out. The sun shone splendidly.

We bought some garlic, onions, cheese, bread and honey and packed them into the Lambretta bag with the methylated spirit stove and some coffee, a Michelin map and a bottle of twelve-degree wine from the wine caves down the street. This was the weather for the canyon. I had heard about this canyon years ago, when I used to live in Nice before the war. For some reason I never got near it, it became a legend, it grew deeper and deeper and more enormous through time. I had made enquiries in various Vence bars, and they all mentioned the gorge of La Loup, about ten miles away. So we set off in the yellow eye of the sun, climbing upwards till we reached La Tourette, stopping in a café opposite the little square and eating the small black olives of the district, sharp with iron and spring oils, and then followed the road to the gorge. On the way, in a small valley, was one of those tiny villages pre-destined for millionaires and their mistresses, slippery with trout out of season, swollen with truffles, and bubbling with champagne. Even the weather was hot, and tall palms sneered from an expensive height. We gazed at it in dismay and con-tinued towards La Loup. Here was the gorge.

Immediately the sun was hidden and the wind stabbed with cold. The gorge was pretty, but small.

"Isn't it wonderful!" I cried as we wound along the road.

Mart stopped and faced me. "It's not," she said. "Face it, it's not. You told me about it in London. You said it was ex-actly like the Colorado canyon. Look at it."

"I'd heard," I said.

"You're an optimist," she cried. "You're a sublime exag-gerator. All your cathedrals are higher than anyone else's, your seas are bluer, your women are prettier, your wine is redder."

This led to an argument and the walls of the inadequate gorge rang with angry definitions of reality. It was an old divergence. Then we continued round the twisting roads and headed back along the other flank of the gorge. High above was Gourdon, a white cloud of a village, and far below lay a great valley rolling down to Nice and the neat blue sea. At first the village astonished; it was wild, cruel and cellar-cool. It is called Gourdon the Saracen, and there is an old Saracen castle, modified in later periods, which we were unable to enter (Sundays in winter 2 to 5). Later in the Vence bars I heard that this château used to belong to a rich American lady, much loved round and about, who, after unwise investments,

269

died of starvation in Nice. Now it is owned by someone belonging to some esoteric religious order who has turned it into a museum, and dark stories go the rounds.

After a walk we perceived that this cloud village had been swallowed by the most execrable modern spider the twentieth century has produced, and its plastic webs glistened everywhere in the cold evening light. GOURDON HONEY shouted huge placards. LAVENDER, ROSE, JASMIN, CARNATION. THE BEST HONEY YOU HAVE EVER TASTED. You couldn't walk for honey stands and neat honey assistants in spotless white, exactly like the bogus doctors in the television commercials. Then there was a frenziedly rustic perfume factory, equipped with retorts and bowls and casks, selling bottles of scent, and presided over by two perfectly type-cast peasants. Mart asked me to sniff bottle after bottle, and I found the perfumes sweet, humble and mountainous. They were also very cheap and I gave her a bottle of Chypre, which she dabbed on her hair. I could smell it, simple mystery, all the way back to Vence.

When we arrived home Pierre told us we had been to the wrong gorge. We should have gone to the gorge of Verdan, about forty miles away.

"Is it bigger?" asked Mart.

"It's enormous," said Pierre, "like the Colorado canyon."

DANCE OF THE ROSES

I BOUGHT some roses for Mart in the market of Vence, while she was buying bones. They didn't look spectacular: small, oval, secretive, dark, rough, red-veined with the rust of rain and *mistral*. But directly they were put in our kitchen they began to open. They were like young girls learning to dance. As the days went by, skirt after skirt dropped to the floor. Their perfume clung gently round your neck and then ran away; the flowers were artless. These roses had nothing in common with the roses of England which always appear to be, at least now, trying to climb the social scale. They have lost their modesty and their perfume. How I hate those huge over-coloured roses in neat suburban gardens, almost intellectual, over-tended substitutes for sex, laughter, or murder. It is the same with English carnations, invariable decoration for Lesbian clubs and promotion waiting-rooms, hard as disguised policewomen. Even the carnations of Provence have nothing in common with these. They haven't been over brought up, they've learned about life in the fields, they haven't even been measured for a dress. It's even doubtful if they are virgins.

The culture of flowers in High Provence is an intense one, but not drawn to your notice over-much. In Vence they

271

grow roses, violets, carnations and orange blossoms. Up above, in the tall hills, lavender. In fact the people there live on lavender, and there is almost too much lavender, too many bees. The lavender world is dying, anyhow; the old ladies are being steadily packed away and the young girls don't care. Mart and I sat in the kitchen, while the bones were boiling, and looked at the roses.

"Draw them," I said.

"Certainly not," said Mart, "I'm not such a fool as that. Go and ask Picasso. He's bought a château near Mougins."

We didn't go to Mougins, we suddenly went to Monaco. We flew through Nice, tasted the spray of a rough green sea, followed the snakings of the corniche, skirting tiny cradled blue bays. In one of them a fat white man in horn-rimmed spectacles lay on a rubber mattress. We sped through a tunnel and charged into Monte Carlo, then on to the Oceanographic Museum in Monaco. Near by was a huge restaurant which we entered for some wine. We would have guessed we were in Monaco because huge arthritic waiters stared at my shoes and the hems of my trousers and then at Mart's rather strange check pantaloons. A party of secure business people were eating lobsters, and one of them, a thin pale man, an obvious mother's dote, giggled at these semi-tropical trouserettes. I made a loud sort of speech in French, and Mart shut me up. We rose, paid and left.

The Oceanographic Museum contains a large hall filled with bottled fish, deep-sea gear and huge marine skeletons. Down below there is a large aquarium and somewhere in the building a research department. It is, without doubt, the most serious oceanographic museum and aquarium anywhere in the world. It was inaugurated by Albert the First of Monaco, who practically devoted his life to the study of exotic fish, and this passionate interest has passed to the present monarch, Prince Rainier. In fact the museum is incomparably more important than the ridiculous, maniac casino which, in most people's minds, summons up Monte Carlo—palm trees, suicides and breaking the bank. At least a great deal of the casino's immoral earnings are swallowed by this aquarium.

The stars of the aquarium are three exhibitionist sea-lions, one male and two obviously seductive females, sinuous as only submarine sin could be. The two wet satin mermaids go daintily at each other's coats, nipping and buffeting in a sort of perfectly evolved ballet, one eye always on the public, whom, from time to time, on top of a diving platform, they actually address. It is not easy to detach oneself from this set performance, and on at least three occasions I had to drag Mart back to the glass windows and the fish she was supposed to be drawing.

These fish are mostly exotic, but some have been taken from the local depths of the Mediterranean, and these are by no means the least interesting. The remaining exhibits have been caught in any of the world's oceans, grotesque, lyrical, sinister and sometimes magical. You can almost hear a thin deep-water music human ears are not made to catch. The most magical, in a pure sense, are the sea-horses who live in a wonderful show-house of coral and deep-sea crannies. They swim with great melancholy, heads bowed, and hover gently, sadly, over a twig or coral, then wrap their tails slowly round it. Here they stay, pausing in the dance, perhaps awaiting some signal, a resolution, a vision. Is it love, is it despair, is it hunger? The questions are absurd, yet these fish almost, dimly, touch chords in our imagination, where others stubbornly resist all claims except fear and startlement.

As striking as the stripes and red noses of the clown-fish, the sober scales of the Grey Surgeons, or the spiny fins, like a galleon's unfurling sails, of the *rascasses*, is the construction of the rocks and sea-bottoms in these wonderful tanks. Here the sea-beasts have get-aways in the crannies, so that Mart, who is really afraid of fish, sometimes started back and away from the glass fronts, as when a sort of spotted dome-fish, like an obscene snake, peeped out of a stony crack and peered at her with tiny, sub-intellectual eyes. (The French name for this individual is *saliste*.)

The most beautiful exhibit of all is what amounts to the dream of all painters, a living picture. Such a statement sounds like bad journalism, but the particular tank to which I refer offers everything that modern art can aspire to or provide, and possesses motion as well. This is a collection of sea-fauna, rooted to their rocky bed, long and tapering like flowers seen through the lenses of a nightmare, or like vegetation on another planet. You observe them, they are still, you stand watching them and sense the ghost of movement, but are not sure. Yet there is a change of composition and presently, eyes, slender tubes, something like truncated yellow gas-pipes, have blossomed with terrible roses and there is a swaying of purple gelatinous pillars, and tentacles sweep the shrimpy waters.

We left the aquarium and drove back along the winding road to Nice. As was customary, we stopped on the way, in a rather dull bar with pastel lemon walls, something like a new public house in an old city. "Now," I said to Mart, "let us see the drawings of the fish."

"What fish?" said Mart in a suddenly harsh voice.

I knew that voice, those bold eyes, the stubborn head like an oak in the gale, it was an instant signal of guilt. I was not, then, her man on an autumn coast, I was her step-father's steps on the stair, the angry dog in the garden, fate like a lost train.

"What fish?" I repeated, stepping into the part. "Indeed, what fish?" I asked.

"Nothing was said about fish," said Mart in a louder voice.

"A lot was said about fish," I cried. "The whole idea was to come here and draw fish."

There was a pause, and she looked towards the door.

"As a matter of fact," she said, "I drew a fish."

"Let me see it," I said.

She began to fumble in one of the large Lambretta bags and drew out her sketch-book. She averted her face, but I could see she was crying. "Here," she said, pointing.

It was the picture of a codfish. Its huge, horrible and unutterably stupid face filled the page. "We have come here," I said, "miles and miles, with the greatest possible difficulty, under hopeless weather conditions, at the mercy of an accountant who hates writers, and we visit the most marvellous aquarium in the world, crammed with the sort of vivid fish that hardly anyone has ever seen, and you draw a *codfish!*"

My own lack of seriousness, my frivolity, my inner disbelief, my courting of catastrophe as a short-cut to joy, was projected into her, into the ever open, bottomless Paradise dustbin which was built into Eve, and into Eves everlasting. It was a mounting row, savage and unfair, because that wasted aquarium, that host of exotic marvels, was my life; I had spurned it too often, starved this sharp, true hunger, and sat bored and boring, talking in the waiting-room. The row fell, lingered and rose again. The codfish became husbands, lovers, treachery, the end of the world and finally exploded in a huge burst of impenetrable silence.

We drove home, and when we climbed the stairs, no word exchanged, we opened the door and our eyes sought the roses. There were no roses. The floor was strewn with petals, and in the round purple bowl were nothing but stems, thorned wood. The dance was over, the tinkling piano locked. It began to rain. I sat at the kitchen table and opened the sketch-book. There were views of Vence, of men playing cards, of the fountain, of the spring of La Foux. On the last page was the codfish. I looked at it for a long time and then sighed.

THE MARBLE FRONTIER

GRADUALLY Vence lent life to our eyes; there was a new, slight charge in our nerves. Since we were poor, there was a certain amount of civilised rebuff, certain attitudes which might be taken this way or that. The French, particularly the French of this part of the coast, not only dislike poverty among men over a certain age, they cannot understand it. They are very hard on any sort of defeat, cruel to the unorganised, terrible to unprotected old age. So I was a writer, and Madame was an artist. Very fine. The Riviera was full of ladies and gentlemen sliding down the backside of the arts. Even if one was good, or too good, or not able to ring the right contemporary combination to bring the francs tumbling out, there were always ways out. Some, in Vence, painters in their own right, like Monsieur Y, did ceramics which they sold to the tourists; others, like Monsieur G, wrote spanking adventure stories, done to a turn with pinches of sadism and genial Gallic freebootery, which were made into films. Nobody, above all here, was taken in. You had to be hard as nails to be a *true one*, drive yourself to the pitch of madness, but Monsieur Y and Monsieur G had steak twice a day, chose the best wines,

276

and entertained their friends. Their coins rang and they were at the mercy of their accountants.

In Vence you drink wine slowly, without the *coitus interruptus* of the English licensing laws, and listen to gossip. You stroll, time slows down, you stand and stare at the street corner, in the grey, rainy square and the buildings compose themselves to a gradual innate satisfaction of the spirit. The people then merge into these still, weathered shapes, the women at the doors of their magic groceries, which are crammed with flowers, sausages, milk, wine, soap, tins of sardines and postcards, and where you can never quite get the object you want, the card-players shouting at the table, jerseyed like macaws, surrounded by old men recalling epics and disasters, a popinjay policeman twirling his cape, the village madman, the randy drunk. The mountain behind, clean as a scrubbed step.

You pick this and that up. Brigitte Bardot's mother and sister live here, this is her home. It is unbelievable. Vence is as prim as a vicarage. It is only a few miles from Nice, but nothing glitters, there are no public butterflies among the sober stores, no restless myth to disturb the ancient order. The newspapers are full of dramas, but they are somewhere else. ASTONISHING HAPPENING AT DINAN. FISHERMAN CATCHES CAR PASSENGER. "Mr. X of Dinan, while out driving peacefully with friends, was the victim of a unique experience. Mr. N of a nearby village, and a noted fisherman, was casting his line into a river, when the hook inadvertently caught itself in the face of Mr. X, who is acting deputy mayor of Dinan. The astonished fisherman, drawing in his line, found himself the possessor, not of the illegal trout he expected, but of a human eye. Mr. X was immediately driven to hospital, where his condition was said to be satisfactory."

There are six art galleries in Vence, one in the street where we lived, and they have more or less permanent exhibitions of international paintings outside the exigencies of "success" or commercialism. We visited one while there was a show of the *collages* of James Vines, an American who lives in Rome, and met the proprietor of the gallery and a sort of assistant, one of those rare middle-aged women whose lines of life and wisdom converge to a sort of perfection. Of course she came from Paris, but spoke a sort of delicate old-fashioned English. This is not a very large gallery, but it gives the impression of being the most important tiny art centre in Europe, and why not? There is a grocer in front, a bar on the side, and three doors further up is the local constabulary. Work goes on in the gallery from early in the morning till late at night. It is selfless work; they are combing the world for signs. The gallery is run by a sort of foundation, and this foundation also provides cheap accommodation for chosen artists.

Suddenly it was All Saints' Day. Neither Mart nor I would ever, normally, have even thought about it; in England it is a day without a curtain. Certainly Mart had returned early from the market and noticed the streets full of people, a certain excitement in the air, and the bells rang louder. We went out to our landlord's bar and drank pastis. It was a very cloudy day. I began to read the *Patriote*. There was the usual attack on de Gaulle and about fifteen murders. A drunken taxi-driver had murdered his whole family with a pick-axe. Radio-active material might still be thrown in the Mediterranean between St. Raphael and Corsica.

"Aren't you going to the cemetery?" cried Madame, the landlord's wife.

"The cemetery?" I said, surprised.

"Certainly," she said, "on All Saints'."

We aren't Catholics, and I mentioned it. She was a shrewd, hard, bitterly integrated person, but she knew the deep facts. "It's got nothing to do with the Catholics," she said. "It's the same for the Protestants or for anybody at all whatever their shape or colour. Don't ask me when it started. We've been visiting the cemetery on this day since the time of Julius Caesar."

You go down the main street and turn right before the bar of the Acacias, go a short way down a yellow road and it is hidden at the end of a narrow turning. There is an archway and those eternal supervisors of the southern underworld, cypresses in uniforms of deep-sea green. It was raining there when we entered, not our rain, but Northern rain, born of the bitter clouds of Leeds and Maidstone, gumboot, lending-library rain, but it couldn't dim, couldn't ever dim, the enormous, triumphant applause of the flowers. They crowded around the graves, deeply partisan, straining their brilliant coloured faces from cut-glass bowls, pots, tissue paper, from the earth itself. Their perfume spiralled in the damp private air, whispering of anything but death, of love on a summer morning, bees and a new book, victorious sopranos, early holidays in foreign trains. Flowers in the South are flowers of life and death. They are carried back and forth between ghost and giver—the frontier here is very thin, it hardly exists. For this reason, in the cemetery pilgrims and celebrants did not possess that sort of devoted mask one is so accustomed to beside Northern graves. Their faces are easy, they stand secure on their magic family circles, gossiping, remembering trivial incidents which, now, are quite outside time. In the North (which of course in a sense may be anywhere) people fear, ignore or are angry with death because they don't really believe in it: at a certain point in childhood or adolescence the road is blocked in love, fate, or near mortality. They are disconnected, always say and do the same things, and pass away like a spent match.

I felt both uplifted and ashamed in this stone anteroom, and so did Mart. Neither of us had any feelings about relations that weren't critical or even hostile. In fact no hand was stretched out. Extreme mother-love, say, in England, is generally only entertained by certain types of people, with unfortunate results of one kind or another, but here, in these more logical lands, this emotional twist doesn't occur. To belong to a family, dead and alive, future, present and past, to stand with flowers before the stone bed which will, some day, enclose you and your children, is the sort of sanity, the only sort of sanity, which has preserved the Mediterranean lands, and which relegates all industry and ambition to its proper and exact place. Mart and myself, and those like us, were chasing sanity. The paths were devious, some of the illuminations were brilliant, but most were lost, and order was difficult to obtain. That neither of us were Christians (in any sense of the word) made no difference at all, this wasn't an ethical place, it was a place of belonging and we were outside it. We would leave the cemetery and see Vence in a different way; the streets would be crossed by threads.

At certain points, going from grave to grave, one was at the exact meeting-point of weeping and laughter, one was involved, one was there. The graves were mostly solid, obeying a pattern: huge stone boxes, plain or ornamented with glazed pansies or roses or surmounted by white plaster figures; and this white, formal tension was resolved by the background of cypresses, dark and complete in passion and philosophy. A very old woman hovered about the paths, she might have been over a hundred, but she walked quite briskly with the aid of a stick, as though she was searching for someone. Perhaps many tombs claimed her, a daughter there, a grandson here, an aunt in one corner, two cousins in another. Perhaps she just wanted the good, sound stone bed, the cosiness of the shades, and the annual tribute of roses, cyclamen and gladioli to gossip about with the ghosts. Near as she was to the frontier, almost merging, she suddenly stopped still in her tracks and stared. She was staring at us. She was staring with a sharp, unwatery eye.

She knew we didn't belong here, that we brought no flowers, no news, we had no white stone door to knock on.

The sun came out. There was a movement of flowers and the sudden hot perfume ran up and down the paths, the tombs shone like chalk, the old woman tapped her way to another part of the waiting-room. Then, in front of one of the graves, blazing with flowers, we saw Pierre, our landlord. He was standing in perplexity, still as a stone, all youth and age naked in his face, like a man on the point of answering an old riddle but no words came. He saw us, we saw that he saw us, but there was no signal of recognition and we passed on.

Next day we went to have our usual morning drink in the square outside Pierre's bar. As he came over to serve us, the bones in his face were contoured by sunlight and he sang of an old sickness like a crackled bell. "It was my brother," he said, with no preamble. "He was blown up by a mine when he was twenty-three. He was a mathematician. Now, at this day, he would be sixty-five and the greatest mathematician in France." He put down the glasses of pastis. "I live," he said.

MIDI MEDITATION

IN ONE OF THE BARS of Vence an artist in ceramics gave me a copy of *Arts* containing an interview with Aragon. The article, very well written by Huguenin, contained some wonderful statements, and one, in particular, struck me. "Realism," he said, "is not photography. The lie is a social means of expressing what cannot be expressed otherwise. If you like, realist art is the *lie* at the service of truth—contrary to what the majority of people think." Certainly contrary to what the majority of people think, above all in England, where the puritanical addiction to "truth" is more important than fulfilment by fantasy, or style, or super-realism. In my own way, I know and have suffered from this, since my writing is composed of exact truths and formalistic lies, like a mosaic, and through this medium I intended a general light of life to filter through. Hence the lofty attacks of literary office men— "frenzied fantasies . . . invention . . . unrealistic clowning!" The "joke" is relegated to the status of the intellectual, dancing badly and heartily at an editorial cocktail party. All right once in a while (like sex), and then back to the serious grind, the strict academic mania.

Then the English papers in Vence. After a few weeks in

the luminous foreign air we started gobbling up the gutter press, this being followed by terrible attacks of indigestion. HOUSEWIVES RIOT OVER H.P. LABOUR ATTACKS SOUR MILK PROJ- ECT. BIGAMOUS LINOTYPE OPERATOR WINS TREBLE POOLS. DUKE OPENS APPLIED SCIENCE EXHIBITION. WIDOW EATEN BY DOGS. The *Telegraph* was better, packed with items which ex- tended the world some little distance from the English Channel. This time it was filled with the court case over Lady Chatterley. A reporter stated, with apparent amazement, that there were no French correspondents at the trial. This amaze- ment was misplaced. The French are deeply and bitterly en- trenched in reality, and have no time to waste over this sort of thing. In fact, they have none of the British preoccupation with the top layer of things, the sort of ethical best Sunday suit, and treat love with neither contempt nor over-reverence. That this enormous pack of highly educated people (at the trial) should spend days publicly kicking "sin" in and out of the dustbin makes one wonder whether any of them are really capable of enjoying certain aspects of life at all. Judged as a serious enquiry into the nature of either literature or life, the case collapsed into a sort of hidebound puerility which could only mean the laughter and anger of the gods.

As it is always flower time in this sheltered part of the Alpes Maritimes, we decided to visit the flower market in the old town of Nice. It is a huge, longitudinal roofed construction furnished with long slabs for displays, and could as well be an emporium for fish, meat, or second-hand clothes. But that didn't matter—there were miles of flowers, regiments of flowers, platoons of roses and mimosa, squads of violets and cornflowers. In November it is almost dangerous for English people to visit such a market, it is like unlimited free wine to a man on the pledge, a glut of lovely girls in a monastery garden, too much innocence for the guilty. Of course, most of these flowers were for death, for the dying. They would go on guard, they would challenge the living under the cypress trees; but the rest were for love. Pinks, for instance, like pretty children panting after running across wet fields, violets from a garden of ghosts, mimosa's lanterns lighting up a winter holiday. Then certain roses, not the ones who go to the opera but those who go to the public dances, drink a trifle too much, giggle and blush, have an affair, marry beneath them and grow fat. We started to buy flowers, enormous bunches of them, had a drink in a market café and kept on being drawn back by an imperative desire to collect more and more, stacking them on the counter of the café until they were a heavenly mountain beside the pastis glasses and the bottles of wine.

Our life in Vence began to centre in the café next door to the art gallery. There was a bar-room, and next door was a restaurant which had been arranged and decorated by Ramel, the ceramist who had formerly worked with Chagall. His artist's fingers, gentle as flowers, had grown hard with business, and the room shone with beautiful, tactful traps to ensnare the traveller, the old wood of the tables glowed with polish, there was a huge open fireplace with a spit, and in front of the garden windows a wicker cage containing four ring-doves. One of these doves formed an enormous attachment for Mart, peering at her, inflating his ringed throat and singing his woodcry of drowned bells. Of course I began to refer to this dove as her boy-friend, and there were constant discussions on the merit of this particular bird. At the end of nearly every argument I would cry, "Then go off to the dove." But something strange happened. When we looked at the cage after a few days, this amorous dove was sitting on a neat nest of five white eggs. It was simply a member of the harem, and the master himself was a dilapidated feather-tangled bird, rheumy in the eye and weak on the leg, not a spark of morning zest left in his frame.

The café was kept by Antoine, an earthy, gay young Provençal, and his wife, pretty, also gay, but perpetually cleaning. Being French, she could of course snap out of her silk dream and be more realistic than all those brave English women who pride themselves on knowing about life. The cocktail of the French spirit is a glass of common sense, a tablespoonful of malice and a dash of innocence—the last ingredient, oddly enough, being very important even on the road to Hell. The clientèle were mixed: students who dropped in to play cards, carpenters, shopkeepers, and elderly laughing men who were somehow anonymous. Ramel was one of the regular visitors, and nearly every evening after stoking up the pottery for his oven he entered the bar to present a bunch of wild herbs to Antoine's wife. It seemed a great moment for him and she played up to it. He knew all the subtleties of cooking and living, but it was a long way down the staircase back to his youth in Paris. "I daren't go back," he said. He had sharp views and a fund of sly stories. He had an enormous antipathy to abstract art—"all the work of Jews and Americans," he said, "like something on the stock exchange. It's a sort of coinage for millionaires' wives. Alimony, mink, European hotels, gigolos with titles, and abstract paintings."

Another client always entered in leggings, with a gun, a couple of hunting-bags and a dog in the offing. He was that rare thing, noble and farcical at the same time. He had long, racy, imperial moustaches, brown as dead bracken, not over-groomed but with a proud, nonchalant air, that of a peasant nobleman. He might have been sixty. He only spoke in Provençal, a language which lends itself, by sound alone, to comedy, exaggeration and magniloquence, a rough round poetry. His stories in the bar were of hunting, a lost rabbit, a missed pheasant, all incidents turned fairly against himself. Fate was obviously set on playing him tricks, although Fate loved him, and he could afford the irreverence of the game.

"He is a happy man," I said to Antoine.

285

"He is a happy man," repeated Antoine.

"Is there anything more than that?" asked Antoine's wife.

"Nothing more," I said.

I looked round the bar and saw other happy men who had never turned their backs on themselves. Unhappiness is, in fact, an enormous area completely off the map, a non-existent disease which is highly infectious. I had been to this area and contracted the disease, quite accidentally, but the effects had lasted rather a long time. In fact I was more like the peasant hunter than the idiot hero.

I had first met the librarian in his shop at the corner of the square when we had gone there to buy maps. He seemed shy, colourless, the typical French proprietor of a provincial book-shop. He even wore a flat black cap to depersonalise his appearance, and carried a high, old-fashioned umbrella in the rain. But in the bar he became not only sharply dimensional-alised, like a dull cloud at sunset, but concentrated in wit, crys-tal deduction and the giddy lightning of destruction. It is never to be forgotten that European civilisation began in the Midi, and that European manners, and even English manners (!), were born there during the glimmer of a supposedly ec-centric poetry in action and expression. It is implicit there, it has not to be over-emphasised or intellectualised, it has the weather on its side, the other side of cruelty's coin is beauty, it is not the clever gentleman's obsession. "Careful, Mr. Carson," the librarian would cry, removing his pedestrian cap, "the gods are laughing." This was because I was flirting with An-toine's wife as naturally as the birds sing at dawn break; it was the movement of a formal dance. In fact the librarian was a sort of eagle, viewing me from a lofty peak, and a thousand years of tolerance stopped him from tearing me limb from limb.

Suddenly, one evening, he turned the bar into the rites of spring, and his elastic-sided boots tripped in Dionysian rhythm as he mimed the seduction of Antoine's wife. It reached a form of perfected frenzy, you thought there could be no further limit, but suddenly his face went impassive and he returned to my table, the lady laughing with delight. Now again he was the librarian, and while the peasant nobleman whistled to his dog, he began talking about Tennessee Williams. "A pure voyeur," he said, "not good enough. The true civilisation requires the service of the lie. The lie, my friend, is at the service of truth, contrary to what the majority of people think."

⎣⎤⎣⎤⎣⎤⎣⎤⎣⎤⎣⎤⎣⎤⎣⎤⎣

CONVERSATION PIECE

RAMEL SEEMED very keen for us to meet a lady called Mrs. Whittaker, who lived a way out of Vence. She was a General's widow, he explained, and, or but, very *spirituelle*. We didn't take advantage of this introduction for some time, because I was waiting for money from England. Various letters had been sent from my bank in London instructing me that the money *should* arrive any day now; obviously the accountant was waiting for the right sort of weather to make up his mind. But the right sort of weather didn't materialise and finally we only had just enough money to drive to Nice, eat maize pancakes in a cheap bodega (an excellent lunch, by the way), and visit the bank. Luckily it was an English one, and a branch of the bank I dealt with in England. In the first place we managed to change a large bundle of sixpences which Mart had been secretly carrying around, tied up in a scarf, and which created something I had never really heard before, laughter in a bank. On top of the laughter came largesse. The manager advanced me ten pounds on sight.

There is something about this sort of money which, though obviously a mere business mechanism, appears like gifts and windfalls and fills the mind with the wind of holidays and

288

reckless hopes. The world, after all, is stacked with money and the most odious people throw it away in roulette, bad books, frightful pictures and all forms of blackmail. How many bores are terribly rich? The result was, we spent it. We started with maize pancakes, and then we went to flowers, and from flowers to arguments, and we were going to part, and there was a terrible scene in the Place Masséna. We drove home through the hot and cold of Fairyland and arrived in Vence. The little flat looked adorable, the Provençal stew was cooking, the flowers flaunting, and there was a new moon in the sky.

The next day Ramel insisted that we meet Mrs. Whittaker. Also, he was suddenly keen to help me with one of my published books, because, it turned out, this lady had read one of them and declared herself in favour of it. I had only one copy and I had intended it to be a sort of passport in any of those countries which Mart and I should happen to visit. "But it's Gallimard," said Ramel, "the most important publisher in France. It would be ridiculous not to try your luck."

"Certainly," I said.

I gave him the copy, and he stared at the picture of the author on the back.

"Who is this elderly gentleman?" he asked, pointing at my photograph.

"It's me," I said.

"I don't believe it," he said, gazing at me incredulously. Only one man had commented in such a fashion, and that was Evelyn Waugh in a review in *The London Magazine*. "Such a face," he hinted, "looks like old —— responding to a heckler during a stormy election, and almost completely invalidates the lyrical interludes of his writing." This was a lot due to the publicity manager of my publishers who had chosen this particular version of my face to exploit an imaginary gimmick, the jolly old boy of Soho, the Jacques Tati of Dean Street, the literary drunk at the mercy of fake French publicans and re-morseless, featureless faces flickering on the bored screen of my consciousness.

I decided to let Ramel have the book, and the next day he disappeared into a sort of Riviera network. There was some sort of go-between who would almost immediately translate my work. The following day he told me this go-between had been very ill in the stomach, and had had to lie on his back in a villa somewhere in St. Raphael.

"But did he look at the book at all?" I asked.

"He was very ill, groaning," said Ramel, "I could hardly get a word out of him."

"But what has happened to it?" I asked.

"He has sent it to Paris," said Ramel.

"And what then?" I asked.

"It will be a very long time before anybody actually does anything about it," he said, and gave me a lot of technical reasons which seemed to pivot on the go-between having suddenly been taken ill in St. Raphael. But I was used to this sort of thing, having spent an expensive week with an American go-between in Paris while he sent off cables to his publishers in Boston, and I still, a year later, receive cheering post-cards saying "Any time now."

Eventually we met Mrs. Whittaker, on her return from Mass in the cathedral, and we had a drink in Antoine's bar. She was a woman of indefinite age, and the winds of the South had almost entirely blown away that sort of Englishness, like the autumn spire of a provincial cathedral, which almost in-variably rises from the bosoms of English ladies abroad. In fact, to add to her innate good breeding, she had absorbed and radiated a sort of off-Parisian elegance, and a sharp wit which mixed attractively with her natural vagueness, leaving everything in shops, and retracing her steps from place to

place like a game of consequences. Her house was in Malbos-
quet, about two miles from Vence, and the outlook was as
beautiful as a child's holiday. The country was swung around
on a kind of revolving stage to show its wildness and terraces
of autumn colours which climbed from russet red to violet
until the white-lipped snow kissed the sky.

Mrs. Whittaker offered us the use of a caravan near her
house, which was actually the property of a retired Air Mar-
shal, and from this site one could look down over the sea.
The area was surrounded by roses, and in the morning large,
burly flower-pickers wound their heavy feet through the
blooms, which then began their voyage to expensive restaurants, managerial board rooms, illicit villas, weddings and
funerals. The weather was soft, the ground was medallioned
with wild flowers and birds sang in the olive trees. Butterflies
danced on the grass. At night, directly over the caravan, an
owl pierced the dark of sleep with love and terror.

One afternoon we had tea in Mrs. Whittaker's house. There
was the usual ritual and fuss, cakes, milk and sugar lumps, but
the ceremony was lightened by the special conversation. Most
conversation, in fact, is creative to the writer's ear, but much
of it has to be sifted and linked by a sort of tedious intellectual
process. Mrs. Whittaker had, as a companion, a governess of
about her own age, of German nationality, who had been employed by her mother. This lady formed a strange but pleas-
ing contrast to the slender-boned framework of Mrs. Whittaker's personality, being heartily sensual, earthy and food-
loving. In the course of a conversation about sea-urchins, Mrs.
Whittaker related that she had been offered the sliced half of
one of these animals by a stall-holder who had cried to her,
"Good for the ovaries!"

"I suppose it means that it's an aphrodisiac," said Mrs. Whittaker, "but I'm sure I don't know if it does any good."

"I do," said the governess in a loud voice, and gave a fat, round laugh which could have issued from the throat of a satiated Rhinemaiden.

The conversation also turned to death, which is a popular topic in the South. There is a kind of final fun about it, fairly delicate and philosophical, less neurotic than the dedicated death-cult of the English intellectual (see Francis Bacon). Mrs. Whittaker told an interesting story. She had a friend in Vence, Madame A, a Frenchwoman who was terribly well-meaning, sociable, absent-minded and essentially kind in the gregarious way that the French of all classes and types are. She was the friend of another French lady, Madame B, who lived in the district, who had an ailing father, convalescent for years, and for whom she always expressed profound concern whenever she happened to meet her. Madame A left Vence for a time and went to Paris, and during this time Madame B's father died. Madame B wrote to her friend in Paris acquainting her of this fact, and in return received heart-felt condolences. Returning from Paris, Madame A dutifully called on her friend, embraced her rapturously, but, in her enthusiasm, forgot all about the death of her friend's father. "And how is your dear father?" she asked after a pause. Then, suddenly aware of her terrible *gaffe*, she rallied and said almost the only thing possible, "Still dead?"

ⅎⅎⅎⅎⅎⅎⅎⅎⅎ

CARSON'S GREECE

A FEW HOURS' JOURNEY across the siren sea from Athens lies the island of Hydra.

It is a fair-sized island, rocky, barren and devoid of water, lying bravely in the blazing eye of the sun. It was one of the places in Greece, if not the only one, which resisted the terrible Turks, and from the café over the battery rocks you can see four or five cannon pointing out to sea.

This island has obviously been discovered many times. Various gods lived there, Pan visited it, Ulysses dropped in; but the deities and semi-deities of Greece like trees, and there are only trees with dappled shade at the northern end of the island and in the café over the battery rocks where, even when the temperature is 110 degrees, there is an almost shivering shade under the gnarled pine trees, and you can get the best *retsina* in Greece.

After many other discoveries, which luckily excluded the Turks, the entry of Pansy should be mentioned. She was a Russian lady, with a face as delicate and strong as a sea-shell, but she could speak almost any other major language with the same degree of fluency and lyrical distortion. Pansy became the queen of the island; she was constitutionally someone

293

who did not avidly require trees, she did not lack water, she made the rocks blossom with her own species of muddled, egotistical flower.

Earlier, in fact, she had been tortured by the Germans when they had occupied the island, but she could still pick up a table with her teeth and dance with the best, her face as hungrily beautiful as a minor goddess, without guilt.

A little later, an Australian and his wife discovered Hydra. They were industrious writers, and on arrival hatched two books, one concerned with packing, the voyage and the first sight of land, and the other a story of primitive love among the islanders, bringing in cicadas, instruments and hastily discovered Greek words.

Finally there was me. I had been staying in the Piraeus in a small hotel which amazingly had turned out to be a brothel, and someone had told me that Hydra was "romantic" in a very special way. What special way? I thought of Pansy and decided it might be true—that and the sun and the sea for which I had now, suddenly, a vast hunger.

I took a boat from the Piraeus and three hours later arrived on the island. You are in the middle of its life immediately: a small rectangular harbour which reminds you of a Cornish seaside village, a film set, a travel poster. There is a faint smell of the past, but everything has been redecorated. It is beautiful but blank. In fact hardly anywhere do you feel the slightest link with the ancient Greece sleeping behind your dreams, only alone, on the jewelled breast of the sea, looking out to the lovely haze of islands, or in the tavern hidden away from the garish port, fathered by its three mystic trees.

I sat in my chosen café, isolated by not speaking the language and by a sad impression that these Greeks were disenchanted, some infinitely valuable spell had been broken, and that they had become utterly mortal. Alas, here they came strolling about in smart kinds of Miami outfits carrying portable radios. You heard snatches of rock'n roll, snippets of exquisite secret country music and the black bigotry of Orthodox church services.

In corners, lumpy children tortured cats, quite a national hobby in a country where they turned mental defectives out into the parks in company with the same sort of children. ("Fresh air is good for them," explained the authorities.) French couples went by, decorously amorous, as though obeying new rules by General de Gaulle, Germans with cameras, and an invasion of Americans, possibly the result of enormous advertisements (in literary form) put out by Mr. Onassis in *Life* magazine, in which this abnormally successful man took over the whole periodical in order to advertise the historical wealth and beauty of his country.

Historical wealth and beauty there is, of course. I unutterably recommend both, particularly the heart-shattering beauty of the islands, but, in a few words, be as alone as possible.

This is nothing to do with youth. Most writers, depending on their age or passions, defend or praise "youth" as though it were a classification which mattered or had any empirical value. I am an over-middle-aged man but I love or hate a number of youths, of both sexes, because of their looks, or sense of the ridiculous, or because of their gallantry to the past (and what is the past but the printed word?). In fact, a number of the new-style American girls attracted me enormously, because their type of desired silliness was better documented than ever and could explain itself in terms of higher applied psychology. Alas, I was baulked.

In no time at all I met a youngish American called Canter who painted brittle, funny, nostalgic paintings collaging playing-cards, love letters from American girls stranded in

Naples and printed notices saying "Address not known." I liked them very much. He spoke Greek and he held the pulse of the islands between finger and thumb.

Among other things, he explained Greek island anthro-political psychology. Love between men on the islands was not intrinsic, it was a matter of necessity, it happened because of the code, and I could sense it was something like Spain. But different. There was more of an act in Greece, it was done with more panache, and, indeed, performance and confidence were highly esteemed and any sort of emotional and physical entanglement was considered more valuable than the terrible, earnest English committees on sexual behaviour. And then there was always a sort of dim, healthy tradition, not based, as in England, on an excess of thought and timidity.

Just as I was beginning to veer sharply towards the young American girls, Canter introduced me to the Vampire of the Islands. Her name was Carlotta. She was sharply perched on the watershed of middle-age, but had not really given up.

Years ago she had been married to an Eastern Prince, and had lived in the sort of palace which was really an annexe, and which didn't give the entire confidence which any woman requires. Finally, of course, the annexe was taken over by the military and then the concubines moved in, and Carlotta went back to Austria, from which she had originated, and lived a chequered life all over Europe, London, Paris and Athens. Oddly enough she knew numbers of my ancient friends, some alive and some dead, some imagined friends and some imagined enemies, and among them was a dead, brilliant man called Brian Howard, with whom I had many terrible skirmishes but who still sparked in my brain like a wonderful, recurring current.

She thought, in fact, I was one of "them," of the old brigade. Evelyn Waugh, Nancy Mitford, and the Duke of Westminster. She was determined about this. This was who I was, and I couldn't possibly avoid it.

She explained everything. I was somehow distinguished, I was somehow the new light on Hydra, the shining modern discoverer. "Nobody really likes the Greeks," she said, "not even the Greeks. Except possibly the Americans, because of Mr. Onassis and Churchill and the rest of the old cream, and there are very few English here, but obviously they are braver than anyone else, like dear old Brian Howard, and they hate the Greeks and the Americans and the French."

Carlotta and I went around quite a bit. "What a liar old Henry Miller was," she said.

"In what way?" I asked.

"In the Colossus," she said, "about smelling old Greece everywhere. What a lie!"

"Perhaps Mr. Onassis?" I said.

We were swimming on the rocks below the cannons, and I was absolutely delighted to see tiny blue and red fish which not only refused to dive away but swam with me. This I loved about the Aegean: I found it again and again, even farther up at the end of the island, where the wasps rasped, far out at sea, at the mouth of my under-water snorkel.

Gradually the strange, exquisite sea-water fields, terraces, forests and weed-poplar cemeteries pulled my eyes down from the sun. It was a sort of lyrical death-wish, sharpened and spiced by the faint possibility of sharks. "Sharks," Carlotta would cry when I was fish-intoxicated in the deep purple water, and there was always the chance. They had first appeared in the Aegean, rumour said, when the troopships of the Second World War were throwing corpses into the sea, but one couldn't be too sure.

Carlotta was not really popular on the island. She was a little too emotionally sophisticated and you couldn't quite exactly hear what she said, but she *knew* certain things and trends very well. When there wasn't anyone with her, the Greeks shouted "Soraya," and afterwards, when I arrived on the scene, there was a certain amount of screaming and shouting and everyone looking obviously normal.

Through her I met some of the new Onassis Americans and, above them in rank, the type of United States citizen-lecturer I would call the American Expressman. Nearly all of them styled themselves as poets, and actually a few of them had published a book which skimmed through Tahiti, Rome, Bangkok, Dublin and London, imperfectly sarcastic (for instance the London section dealt inadequately with dogs, Rome with the Hotel Danieli and gondolas, Dublin with the topside of the Blarney Stone and Tahiti with a pygmy all-in wrestler). Their brains moved at the speed of light, their hearts were in the wrong place, and they filled all the islands with a terrible off-beat sort of aesthetic disease which will eventually engulf the whole world, and all non-American poets will have to live in Blackpool or Dieppe.

But some of the American girls glowed like petunias. I met them on the rocks and we went diving for fish and pushing each other into the water. All of them had university degrees, were writing books and ordered people about. They had hard centres, determined ideas which they launched like missiles, but could change into salt-kissed kittens at the drop of a bathing-cap.

I used to meet them around the harbour, fluttered at them and felt the years slipping away. One was called Laura, the least worldly of the lot, not an American Expresswoman. I used to ask her for drinks round at my café, but Carlotta was terribly rude. "She's agonisingly silly," she said. "You're too old and distinguished for that sort of nonsense. You need distinguished people." I immediately agreed with her as I agree with everybody but perhaps not about age. Hadn't I really come to Hydra to drink the spring water of youth?

One day I discovered Laura alone in a secluded corner of the rocks and we went diving for fish. Almost accidentally we caught one and brought it out of the water. It was pale pink with blue eyes and fluttered gently in the doom of Laura's palm.

We were bent together, examining it, when we heard Carlotta's Vienna Woods voice above our heads. "What have you got?" she cried.

"A fish," said Laura.

"That," cried Carlotta, picked it out of Laura's hand, and threw it back into the sea.

The next morning I asked Carlotta about the incident of the fish. "Those fish are as common as dirt in Hydra," she said. "Nobody looks at them except the weekend Greeks and the Americans. The main trouble with you is that you get over-enthusiastic. It could spoil you as an objective writer."

I pondered this for an hour or two, and came to the conclusion that she was right. I didn't dive for the fish any more with the American petunias. But I began to feel quite a lot older.

I had been on another Greek island for quite a while before it gradually came to my attention that I was going to be stranded.

Such is my way, I have huge optimisms, make plans, and then doubt gnaws among the roses. Certainly this was the wrong island to be stranded on; you would have to throw yourself at the mercy of Americans, who would kick you in the teeth and quote Robert Frost at the same time. I wanted something fairly idyllic, an island of pipes, my own island in fact. And somewhere there was such an island, a day's journey away, burning with beauty and stark as a bone.

I started to write begging letters, sent them off, and waited in my false paradise. Cyclops is a lovely island, but Hollywood used it for a film and ever since then it glistens in a sort of hardly perceptible cellophane. Then, one day, I went to the post-office and received a letter from my publisher. He stated that, with much reluctance, he had sent me money directly on receipt of my letter. It should have arrived days ago and had been wired to my very island. Anthony Carson, Cyclops. This filled me with relief, if not joy. It wasn't a large sum, not enough to sail into lost time over fragile seas, nor to plan a slow seduction of the smart, hard, innocent American girls who blazed through the island. It was enough, however, to get leisurely back to England, stopping a bit for a certain lack of enthusiasm.

I began to haunt the tiny post-office. It was staffed by the usual sadists who run post-offices, prisons and public schools. The Greeks love money, and these officials had special organs to smell it out. People below a certain income level were made to wait for hours outside the mail-department and return at doubtful hours when the post-office might be shut. Women were turned away for being incorrectly dressed; their dogs were incarcerated; there was no one to appeal to because there was nothing to appeal to. When I first applied for my money, a man with a priest-like face burst into rocky laughter and peered at me through the grille. "How much?" he asked. I mentioned the sum, and his face came closer. "There is no bank on the island," he said.

Then I got drunk. It was the first time I had got drunk on the island, and everybody looked as if they were employed by the post-office. I told them so. A Greek and his wife took exception to my remarks. He was an ex-Oxford man, with the slack, thoughtful look of the Cornmarket, and his wife was Dutch. "It is not true," he said; "all Greeks are not employed by the post-office. For one thing there are not enough post-offices. Secondly you risk being thrown in the harbour. And thirdly there is a sort of bank here. It does certain kinds of transactions, I think." He gave me the address.

I went to the address and found a tiny office with a huge desk and papers on it, and on one of the papers I could see a small spider. It was dead. I hung about in the bars near the crypto-bank, until suddenly I found it open. There was a man behind the desk, and he looked up at me with the instant recognition of hatred. "What do you want?" he shouted. I stated my case, and the lenses of his spectacles glinted with derision. "There is no money here," he said, "I do not deal in money. Go to the post-office." I went back to the post-office, back to the bank, back to the post-office. Everybody on the island knew the sum of money I was going to receive, that I was going to Istanbul, Cairo and then on to Honolulu.

Finally I left the island and returned to Athens. Somebody had told me that money drafts went round Greece in a circle, and this one could have rolled back to the capital. I had very little money—a fact that wouldn't have worried me once with youth in the bank and a jolly profile—and I felt a sort of hollow in my stomach like an adventure going bad. But, in fact, the money *was* in Athens, deep-down in the vault. I shook hands with numbers of directors and bought a ticket for London via Brindisi and Venice. "It's a new boat on its first run," said an official. "Swimming bath and top-grade luxury. It's called *Perseus*. Have a good trip."

Two days later I boarded *Perseus*. It was covered with rust and an "e" of *Perseus* had fallen off. "This way," said a steward and led me down to the very bottom of the ship; you couldn't have gone lower. "Here, sir," said the steward, opening a door. I was met by a terrible blast of heat, it was like Hell. The whole cabin was lined with waterpipes; I was in a tiny walled-in extension of the engine-room. "It'll be all right when we get under way," said the steward.

When the ship did get under way, I returned to the cabin and found it hotter still. There were no portholes and the ventilators weren't working. There was a minute sigh of air on the top bunk under which I lay, naked, sweating into the sheets. I went up on deck, had a meal, and decided to sleep on deck, taking up a pillow and a blanket. I had fallen asleep for a few hours, when somebody shook me. "Against the regulations," said one of the stewards. "And please don't shout so loud; there are first-class passengers sleeping."

The next morning I was sitting in a bar over an *ouzo* when I became aware of a young man beside me drinking double whiskies and smelling, very simply and directly, of money. We began talking, and he told me he came from Boston. "I've been on this appalling ship three times," he said, "and it is growing steadily worse. They know me. Especially him." He pointed towards a sort of sergeant-major who seemed to be the chief steward. I was certain that the American could have bought the whole ship, if not the line. "Why don't you fly?" I asked him.

"Something to do with an emotional ratio," he said. "A purely American complex. This is the only place where anyone is rude to me. And that is the only man." Again he indicated the sergeant-major. The Bostonian's name was Conrad. He belonged to a Catholic family, and although good-looking and virile enough to be a film-star, fenced himself off from girls, not leaping the first hedge.

After lunch I decided to beard the sergeant-major about my cabin. He was extremely paternal and actually patted me on the back as if I was his favourite corporal. "After Brindisi," he said in Bronx English. But for some reason or other, the ship was held up interminably in Brindisi, and by nightfall nobody gave a thought about cabins. Also the ship was going to be four hours late at Venice, losing all the train connections, the love connections, the money connections. Twice the sergeant-major shouted at me.

The next time I met Conrad we decided to sabotage *Perseus*, and made a plan of campaign. The next day as the ship approached Venice, we began flooding the water-closets and then threw masses of crockery into the sea, pretending to stumble over each other as we pointed at passing ships. Finally Conrad produced an enormous conch-shell which he had found on some island beach and which he had marvellously learnt to blow. We stood directly below the bridge and the smart young Bostonian blew the Emergency signal, Abandon Ship. He blew it three times, astonishingly loud, and then hid the conch in a bag on his arm. A few seconds later three or four officers pattered down the gangway and questioned the passengers. Some of these were laughing; they had seen the manœuvre, and there was an air of mutiny. Then we went down to the disembarkation point, opposite the purser's office, glasses of *ouzo* in our hands, and slapped the sergeant-major on the back (Conrad wanted to push him into the sea). "Good luck," we said, raising the *ouzo*.

"Good luck," shouted the sergeant-major, laughing. It was childish, but we had both climbed through a wreck of dreams and drowned mermaids; Greece was exposed as a hymn of portable radios. Conrad peeped over his well-trimmed hedge; I, with my growing years, began to plant one.

The gang-plank was now in position; and, as we saw the water from the WCs flowing down the staircase, we ran quickly down into Italy. An hour later we were sipping cocktails in the Danieli, and everyone was bowing. "You know what?" said Conrad, nodding back to the waiters. "That sergeant-major looked exactly like my father."

OFF THE MAP

I HAD NEVER BEEN stuck in London so long. I'd tried Putney Bridge, Hither Green, Earl's Court and the backwater of the Fulham Road, but it was still London, they still shouted "Time Gentleman Please" and the buses still crawled down the Holloway Road in reluctant bunches of three, a sort of mechanised Holy Trinity. The fog coiled round the corners of the streets and licked the window-panes and you couldn't see the sky. I was coughing like an old dispersed lion. I needed a change, mountain air, wine festivals, an old train rattling through the foreign night.

One afternoon I was standing coughing in the Chaos Club waiting for something to turn up, a contract, a seduction or even a drink, when I was approached by a tall thin man with side whiskers and a limp. I vaguely remembered his face and he was well dressed enough, in a flashy sort of way, for at least a glass of Guinness or even two.

"Hullo," he said, holding out his hand, "you're Carson, aren't you?"

"That's right," I said.

"My name's Spandle. Jock Spandle. You may remember me. We were both in the travel game a couple of years back.

We met on the Montreux run. You haven't forgotten Gladys, have you?"

"No," I said.

"We're married now," said Spandle with a wink. "Two kids."

"Congratulations," I said.

"You still in the courier game?" he asked.

"No," I said, "I'm writing."

"Writing," said Spandle, raising his eyebrows, "that's a mug's game, isn't it? Why not do something with class? Come back to the racket, and I'll give you a job. Twenty smackers a week, expenses, commission knock-off, and all the gratuities."

"It's an idea," I said, already breathing the mountain air.

A week later I met Spandle at Blackbush airport. I'd managed to borrow a suit and have a hair-cut, and Spandle gave a nod of congratulation. "No one would guess you were a writer," he said. He introduced me to thirty clients, and I soon found myself back in the travel-world dialect. Then I took him aside. I felt rather worried.

"Where on earth are we going?" I asked.

"That's the whole point," said Spandle with a laugh. "It's a mystery trip."

"Mystery?" I said.

"Certainly," said Spandle, "it's booked like that." He took out a brochure and handed it to me. "MYSTERY FORTNIGHT BE-HIND THE IRON CURTAIN. ONE HUNDRED GUINEAS ALL IN."

"Good God," I said, "but what about my passport, visas?"

"Don't worry about that," said Spandle, "it's all arranged. Influence." The propellers whirred and we zoomed into the sky. "We'll be flying all night," said Spandle, "sweet dreams."

The next morning, early, I woke up and peered through the window down at a range of hills and a small mountain.

"Is this Russia?" asked a stout lady in a hard pink hat.

"More like Rumania," said a man behind her, "I was there in 'twenty-nine. On government business. Remember the geography."

"Hope we get *out* all right," said rather a pretty girl nervously.

"Courier," shouted a voice on my right, "where are we?"

"I'm not allowed to divulge," I said, "official secrecy regulations. Fasten your safety belts." The plane circled and landed on a strip of tarmac. We got out and I helped Spandle direct the passengers through the customs and police sheds. Then we drove off in a motor-coach to a large village, almost a small town, and arrived at a brand-new hotel with an illegible name. I allotted rooms to the clients, and then went down to the bar and had a drink with Spandle.

"What'll you have?" I said.

"Vodka," said Spandle.

"There's only vodka or slivovitz in the town."

We drank vodka, and a few local residents joined us, talking a melodious sort of language I couldn't place. One or two of them spoke English, and they politely welcomed us to their country.

At dinner, the perplexed clients ate highly spiced food and the local singers came in and serenaded us. "It's Rumania all right," said the man who had spoken to me in the aircraft, "I remember the food and the dialect and you can distinctly trace the Latin blood. Look at that waiter, for instance."

"More like the Crimea," said an elderly gentleman opposite him.

"I think the food's horrible," said the lady in the pink hat.

"Then you should stay at home," said the elderly gentleman.

"Or try and broaden your mind," said the other.

After dinner, Spandle got up and made an announcement. "Ladies and gentlemen," he said, "I trust you have eaten well.

You are free this evening, but kindly stay in the hotel as the authorities have lately imposed a curfew."

"A curfew," shouted a voice, "do you mean they'll shoot?"

"Possibly," said Spandle.

"It's disgraceful," said the same voice. "I could have been in Menton. We'll all end up as political prisoners."

"I think it's rather fun," said a woman with a nervous giggle.

"In the morning," continued Spandle, "there will be conducted visits to factories, sports arenas and housing estates. In the evening there will be a concert followed by regional dancing. I would like to impress on you the importance of staying together in a group, as I cannot be responsible for anyone lost."

The next morning we awoke to the sound of firing. At breakfast Spandle did his best to pacify the clients. "A small local uprising," he explained, "and I have been informed that the authorities have dealt with it. The coach will be here at nine o'clock sharp." When we reached the bicycle factory and handed the group over to a guide, Spandle and I went to have a drink. He left the bar for a moment and I got into conversation with a red-faced man in a cloth cap.

"You speak good English," I told him.

"Thank you," he said.

"Do you come from this village?" I asked.

"No. From the nearest town," he said.

"You may think it an odd question," I said, "but could you tell me where I am?"

"Where you are?" cried the man in the cloth cap, "why, you're in Wales." He looked at me with sharp curiosity and went off to drink by himself, eyeing me from time to time over the rim of his glass.

When Spandle came back I told him I knew everything.

"You had to find out sooner or later," said Spandle.

"But what about the firing this morning?"

"A shooting range behind the hotel," said Spandle. "It's a pity about these odd visitors. I'm making arrangements to tighten up security. After all, the town's getting the money out of us. I'll see the Chief Constable this afternoon."

When the fortnight was over, we flew back to London, and generally speaking the Mystery Tour clients were thoroughly satisfied. "Better hotels and service than anywhere in England," said the old gentleman who thought he had been in Rumania. He gave me a tip of two pounds. I had the telephone numbers of two of the girls.

A month later letters began to appear in the press. One was in the *New Statesman* and began: "Sir—after a visit to Eastern Europe, in which I was free to go where I wished, and speak to whom I wished, I would like to express my impressions of the great reforms that have been carried out by the people. I visited a bicycle factory, a soda-syphon assembly unit, and the headquarters of a thriving tinned milk industry. I found labour conditions, hygiene and welfare services better than any in this country. This was an independent visit, organised by a normal travel agency (Mystery Tours) which . . ."

But it was all over in two months. There was a headline in the *Sunday Pictorial.* "Travel dupes pay to go behind the Iron Curtain, are flown to Wales." This was accompanied by a photograph of Spandle in profile. THIS MAN IS A FILTHY CROOK, said a sub-title, followed by a confession extorted by a special correspondent. Months later I met Spandle in a pub in Chelsea. He seemed very cheerful and better dressed than ever.

"I did pretty well out of it, all considered," he said, offering me a Guinness.

"But who gave the game away?" I asked.

"It was by arrangement," said Spandle with a grin. "The

Welsh Nationalists gave me a thousand pounds to publish the name of the town. You've got to move quick in this lark. You gone back to writing?"

"Yes," I said.

"You won't make anything out of that," said Spandle. "Now I've got an idea . . ."